John McCormick is a British █████████████████████████
and reports have appeared in ██████████████████████████
the world. His other books, █████████████████████████
(1985) and *The Global Envir*████████████████████████
known. He is, at the time of publication, lecturing and completing
his PhD in political science at Indiana university.

Acid Earth

The Global Threat of Acid Pollution

John McCormick

EARTHSCAN PUBLICATIONS LTD   London

This second edition published in Great Britain 1989
by Earthscan Publications Limited
3 Endsleigh Street, London WC1H 0DD

British Library Cataloguing in Publication Data

McCormick, John, 1954-
    Acid earth: the global threat of acid pollution. - 2nd ed.
    1. Environment. Pollution by acid rain
    I. Title
    363. 7'386

ISBN 1–85383–033–X

Earthscan Publications Limited is an editorially
independent and wholly owned subsidiary of the
International Institute for Environment and Development (IIED)

Typeset by Selectmove, London
Printed and bound in Great Britain by
Guernsey Press Co. Limited, Guernsey, C.I.

Front cover: Acid fog affecting the health of the trees in the Black Forest, West Germany, Adam Hart Davis/Science Photo Library.

Back cover: Deformed embryo of the spotted salamander raised experimentally in low pH H_2O levels similar to those found in acid-rain contaminated waters, T. P. Dickinson/Science Photo Library.

Contents

Abbreviations and Acronyms

CEGB	Central Electricity Generating Board (UK)
CEQ	Council on Environmental Quality (US)
CSAV	Czechoslovak Academy of Sciences
CSE	Centre for Science and Environment (India)
EB	Executive Body (of ECE convention)
EC	European Community
ECE	United Nations Economic Commission for Europe
EDF	Environmental Defense Fund (US)
EMEP	Co-operative Programme for Monitoring and Evaluation of Long-Range Transmission of Air Pollutants in Europe
EPA	Environmental Protection Agency (US)
FBC	fluidized bed combustion
FGD	flue gas desulphurization
LDCs	less developed countries
LIMB	lime injection in multistage burners
LRTAP	Co-operative Technical Programme to Measure the Long-range Transport of Air Pollution
MAFF	Ministry of Agriculture, Food and Fisheries (UK)
MDCs	more developed countries
MOI	Memorandum of Intent on Transboundary Air Pollution (US/Canada)
MW	megawatt
NAPAP	National Acid Precipitation Assessment Program (US)
NCAC	National Clean Air Coalition (US)
NCB	National Coal Board (UK)
NCC	Nature Conservancy Council (UK)
NICs	newly industrialized countries
NRC	National Research Council (US)

OECD	Organization for Economic Cooperation and Development
OME	Ontario Ministry of the Environment (Canada)
PFBC	pressurized fluidized bed combustion
UNECE	*see* ECE
UNEP	United Nations Environment Programme
WHO	World Health Organization

CO	carbon monoxide
CO_2	carbon dioxide
HC	hydrocarbons
HNO_3	nitric acid
HO	hydroxy radical
H_2O_2	hydrogen peroxide
H_2SO_4	sulphuric acid
NO_2	nitrogen dioxide
NO_x	nitrogen oxides
O_3	ozone
pH	potential hydrogen (measure of acidity/alkalinity)
SO_2	sulphur dioxide

Acknowledgements

The genesis of *Acid Earth* has depended very much on the input and the views of others. I owe much to Jon Tinker and Lloyd Timberlake for getting me involved in the project in the first place, and to the UN Environment Programme (UNEP), which provided the funding for the first edition.

I would also like to thank Britt Aniansson, who made a considerable contribution to the early drafts of the first edition. Individual chapters were reviewed by several people who added notably to the quality and accuracy of the text. In Britain, I would like to thank David Baldock and Ronald van der Giessen of the Institute for Environment and Development (IIED), Nigel Haigh of the Institute for European Environmental Policy, Dr Neil Cape of the Institute of Terrestrial Ecology, and especially Dr Martin Holdgate (now director-general of the International Union for Conservation of Nature), who took considerable time to review and work through the first two chapters of the first edition with me. In the United States, I would like to thank Betsy Agle of the National Clean Air Coalition and Bob Yuhnke of the Environmental Defense Fund for their help, and in West Germany, Rainer Griesshammer of the Öko-Institut in Friëburg, and Hubert Meiners of the Bund Deutscher Landschafts-Architekten e.V. Adele Hurley of the Canadian Coalition on Acid Rain, Karen Rajeandran of Sahabat Alam Malaysia, and my former Earthscan colleagues Jacqui Craw and Consuelo Green provided me with useful additional sources of information. And I would like to thank the reviewers of the first edition, many of whose comments helped amend or reinforce the second edition.

John McCormick
Indianapolis, Indiana
June 1989

Introduction

In 1852, a 35-year-old Scottish chemist studying the quality of air in and around his adopted home of Manchester found local rainfall to be unusually acidic. Robert Angus Smith had long been concerned about the way industry could pollute air and water. He suspected a connection between the acid rain and the sulphur dioxide given off when coal was burned by local factories. He even noticed that the acid in the air was causing the colours of textiles to fade and metals to corrode. Twenty years later, after more fieldwork in England, Scotland and Germany, Smith published his findings in his book *Acid and Rain: The Beginnings of a Chemical Climatology*. In it, he spelled out the link between sulphur pollution and what he called "acid rain". He showed how the chemical make-up of rain, fog and snow could be affected by wind direction, proximity to the sea, and the amount and frequency of rain and snow. He drew up a detailed strategy for analysing the chemistry of precipitation, and warned that acid rain was damaging plants and materials.

Very few heeded these warnings until almost a century later, when research in Western Europe and North America reconfirmed Smith's discoveries. Sulphur and nitrogen oxides produced when oil, coal, natural gas or peat were burned could be converted in the atmosphere into sulphates and nitrates, and then into acids, which could return to earth in contaminated rain, snow, hail, fog or mist. Scientists in Scandinavia, West Germany, Canada and the United States began to sound alarm bells. Their research revealed widespread – and rapidly growing – damage from acid rain. By the late-1970s, acid rain was a major environmental issue. Today, the effects sound an all too familiar litany.

○ Trees are being killed or damaged, and soils left too acid to support plants. More than two-thirds of all the United Kingdom's forests – and more than half of those in the Netherlands, Switzerland, and West Germany – are damaged. In parts of Europe and the United States, crop yields are being cut. Eleven European countries may be losing crops worth as much as $500 million per year. In the United states, the losses may be worth as much as $3 billion per year.

○ Lakes are turning acid. In southern Norway, one lake in five is either dead or dying. In Sweden, 20,000 lakes are acidified, and a fifth of those have no fish. In Ontario, Canada, nearly 50,000 lakes are vulnerable; fish and aquatic plants are dying.

○ In smog-bound cities throughout the world, people with respiratory and heart complaints are ailing, even dying, from acid smoke and dust pollution. The infamous winter smog of 1952 hastened the deaths of at least 4,000 Londoners. In two days in August 1984, 500 Athenians were hospitalized after a smog so severe that emergency government measures had to be imposed to protect the health of the population. In Mexico City, one of the most polluted cities on earth, the mayor has warned of "collective hysteria" unless dramatic action is taken to reduce air pollution. More cars on American roads has meant more pollution in American cities; more than 100 US cities exceeded recommended ozone levels in 1988.

○ Stone buildings are being eaten away. In parts of Poland, railway tracks have been so corroded that trains must slow to a crawl, and the gold on the roof of Krakow's cathedral chapel is dissolving. Acid pollution may be causing corrosion to cars in Canada. On London's St Paul's Cathedral, which survived a wartime blitz, lead grouting now stands an inch proud of the external stonework.

○ The earliest damage was found in Scandinavia and Canada, downwind from the industrial centres of central Europe and the American mid-west. Research has since found acid damage through most of Western and Eastern Europe, in the eastern and western United States, Soviet Union, and – more worryingly – in less industrialized countries. China has growing acid pollution problems, and winds may be blowing the pollution to Japan. In

India, the Taj Mahal is dissolving in an acid wind. Acid deposition has been found downwind of the Zambian copperbelt. In Johannesburg, buildings are corroding. Soil samples in Brazil have shown unusually high acid levels. Even in the Arctic, hundreds or thousands of miles from the nearest industrial centres, atmospheric haze has turned experimental filters grey.

Acid rain has become one of the quintessential global environmental issues. It has tested the ability of our economic and political systems to respond to the growing destruction of the environment, and shown only too obviously how confused, divisive and piecemeal are those systems. The confusion shows itself in the three dimensions of the acid rain problem.

First, there is the scientific dimension. The phrase "acid rain" makes good newspaper copy, but it is not altogether accurate. As Martin Holdgate (former chief scientist of the UK's Department of the Environment) observes, acid deposition is "a much broader process than has often been assumed, involving interactions between many atmospheric pollutants and several pathways. We ought to stop describing it by the generic term 'acid rain'". Acid pollution is caused by the sulphur dioxide (SO_2), nitrogen oxides (NO_x), hydrocarbons (HC) and ozone produced when coal, oil, natural gas, peat and other fossil fuels are burned. Acting alone or together, these chemicals can produce acidic pollutants that are wet (rain, snow, mist) or dry (gases, particles, smog). The pollution itself is not always "acid", but may trigger off acidification in soils, lakes and rivers.

Confirming and agreeing the causes, effects and scale of acid pollution has not been easy. Scientists are beginning to agree, but the mechanics of acid pollution are still disputed and debated. Monitoring and data gathering systems differ from one country to the next. Even within countries, data from government, industry and independent scientists may not agree. New theories about sources and effects emerge all the time. On the question of forest damage alone, at least 186 different hypotheses have been outlined.

Second, there is the political dimension. The lack of agreement among scientists has been regularly used by governments and industries to oppose action. But these have been little more than excuses, often concealing government unwillingness to upset regional or or industrial lobbies opposed to acid rain controls. In early 1983, the Canadian Environment Minister John Roberts argued that there was enough information to act, and that it was no longer a question of science, but of political will: "We have reached the point where a decision to stall and drag our feet on the pretext that we need more research is, in fact, a decision to do nothing". In July 1985, Dr Mostafa Tolba, director of the UN Environment Programme, said that the public was "right to expect governments to take ameliorative action. They are right to be impatient, if not suspicious, when action is delayed pending further research". In 1989, President George Bush said the time for study alone had passed; "the time for action is now". Within months, he had proposed extensive new legislation to reduce SO_2 and NO_x emissions.

Part of the problem lies in the nature and structure of our political institutions and political culture. Few countries have systems capable of dealing with holistic planning problems. Short-term local interests continue to outweigh long-term universal concerns. Within countries, acid pollution has pitted the needs and priorities of industry against those of agriculture, the needs of one region against another. Because fossil fuel emissions in one country are often converted into acid deposition in another, acid pollution has become an international issue as well. But we do not yet have the political will or the institutions capable of addressing broad-ranging problems quickly and effectively.

Finally, there is the economic dimension. How much are we prepared to pay for a clean environment? Who is going to have to pay? Can conventional benefit-cost analysis be applied to questions as big and as nebulous as air pollution? The costs of controls are relatively easy to calculate – the cost of switching from high-sulphur coal to clean coal, the cost of fitting scrubbers to power stations, and the cost of fitting filters to vehicle exhausts. Much less easy to calculate is the often theoretical cost of a lack of action: the costs that may come from dead forests, acid lakes, lost crops, corroded buildings, and declining human health. And how are priorities logically to be weighed against other urgent problems, such as tackling homelessness and poverty, controlling drugs, dealing with racism, or combatting AIDS?

Since the Swedes first drew international attention to the problem of acid rain, it has become a major public policy issue. But the emotional and often angry debate between and among governments and non-governmental organizations has often clouded the distinction between fact and fiction, and has confused the scientific and political dimensions of acid pollution. *Acid Earth* is a response to the confusion. First published in 1985, it is still the only study of acid rain as a global problem or as a public policy problem. It sets out to describe the dimensions of acid pollution and to assess the possible responses. It argues that acid rain – like many other environmental problems – has many dimensions, but that it is ultimately a political problem that can only be adequately addressed by changes in public policy. *Acid Earth* also argues that such changes can only begin once a problem is fully recognized, and its parameters understood. The first three chapters are devoted to the causes and consequences of acid pollution, and to an examination of the possible responses. Chapter 4 looks at acid pollution as an international policy problem. The last five chapters then look at national and regional examples, outlining experiences in thirty-four countries.

Anyone who writes a book about an issue that changes and develops as quickly as acid pollution has to be prepared to make some major changes in later editions. Not only is our understanding of the acid rain problem constantly growing and improving, but the political response has been changing. An additional level of complexity is added by the fact that the first edition of *Acid Earth* was one of a series of paperbacks aimed specifically at providing journalists, non-governmental organizations and educationists with an easily accessible source of information on a complex topic. As such, it concentrated on describing the mechanics of acid pollution and cataloguing the extent of the damage, without going too deeply into the nature of acid pollution as a public policy issue.

Since the first edition was published, I have spent three years working on a doctorate in political science at Indiana University in the United States. Inevitably, my focus and emphasis has shifted. This second edition provides a description of the problem as before in the hope of helping readers make sense of the scientific and economic complexities of the problem, but it also devotes more space to a discussion of policy responses: what are governments doing, why are they doing it, and what should they be doing? And what does the record of international efforts to reach agreement on acid pollution say about the future of efforts to reach agreement on other global environmental problems?

Of all the changes that have taken place since 1985, perhaps three stand out.

First – as the first edition prophesied – the United Kingdom reversed its position on acid rain, and is now committed to major reductions in sulphur dioxide and nitrogen oxides by the beginning of the next century. This left the United States alone among industrial democracies in refusing to take action; but that has now changed with George Bush, who is taking a more constructive and active approach to the environment than his predecessor.

Second, there has been a change of attitude (if not yet in policy) in the Soviet Union, the biggest single source of acid pollution in the world. Mikhail Gorbachev has called for new co-operation in addressing global environmental issues. What this will mean in real policy terms remains to be seen.

Third, the public debate about acid pollution seems to have been by-passed to an extent by the new debates about the ozone layer and the greenhouse effect. But this does not mean that acid rain has gone away, or that environmentalists can rest on their laurels. Although many countries have now committed themselves to dealing with acid pollution, and although some have already cut their SO_2 and NO_x emissions by 25–50%, several questions remain:

1. Can all those countries which have promised to reduce their emissions actually meet their commitments? Many already have, but some are proving much slower.
2. Emission reductions of 25–50% are welcome, but will they be enough? Will further reductions be needed, will they be possible, and will they be made in time to avoid more damage?
3. Despite all the cutbacks in emissions, much damage has been done, and has still to show itself. What kind of long-term changes will make themselves felt in the next 20–30 years? Will policy-makers learn anything from the long-term costs of their refusal to take short-term action?

4. Events in the Soviet Union notwithstanding, emissions in some of the centrally planned economies are on the increase; between 1980 and 1984 Yugoslavian emissions grew by 53%, and between 1985 and 1990 Polish emissions are expected to grow by 20%. What can be done to reverse these trends?
5. The movement to win international agreement on emission reductions has so far centred almost exclusively on the industrialized world, and has all but ignored the less developed countries. But early estimates suggest the potential for major acid pollution problems in China, Malaysia, the Philippines, India, Brazil, Mexico and other countries. What can be done to avoid these problems?

These are some of the questions developed in this second edition of *Acid Earth*. It has been completely revised and updated to take account of developments since June 1985. Chapters 1 and 5 have been rewritten. A new conclusion has been written in an attempt to place the acid rain problem in context within the changes that have taken place in global politics, and to assess the extent to which action on acid rain sheds light on the potential for future action on other global environment problems.

1. The Formation of Acids

A casual observer could be forgiven for thinking that acid pollution was a relatively recent – and sudden – problem. Twenty years ago, it was almost unknown to anyone but a handful of scientists. Today, it is a critical scientific, economic and political problem, straining relations between normally friendly governments, pitting polluters against polluted, and testing the will and the ability of policy-makers and political systems to respond to major environmental issues.

Yet pollution from coal-burning has been a problem for more than 800 years. During the reign of Edward I of England (1272–1307), a Royal proclamation was issued prohibiting the use of sea-coal (coal washed ashore from exposed coal deposits) because of the smoke it produced; a third offence was punishable by death.[1]

During the seventeenth century, the naturalist and diarist John Evelyn campaigned vigorously to have something done about air pollution in London. Evelyn complained of the "Hellish and dismall Cloud" which made London resemble "the suburbs of hell".[2] He thought some of this pollution was being blown across the channel to France, and recommended that industry be moved out of towns, and that taller chimneys be built to disperse the pollution. Common law provided some protection from specific nuisances. For example, a complaint against a London baker in 1691 from one of his neighbours resulted in an order for the baker to build a chimney "soe high as to convey the smoake clear of the topps of the houses".[3]

Despite half-hearted attempts to control emissions from steam engines during the early stages of the Industrial Revolution, the spread of industry brought increasingly polluted air to the towns and cities of the United Kingdom. The issue was finally brought to parliament in 1819, and in 1821 the first law was passed aimed at reducing smoke from steam engines. But loopholes and exemptions ensured that it achieved little. In 1845, *The Times* noted in an editorial that "the evil of smoke has reached a most intolerable height".[4] The United Kingdom – the cradle of the Industrial Revolution – had become the most polluted country on earth. In 1853, a Smoke Nuisance Abatement (Metropolis) Act was passed. Promoted by Lord Palmerston during his tenure as Home Secretary, the act applied only to London. Although 6,500 offenders came under investigation in the first year, only 124 were convicted.[5]

In 1862, the question of the pollution created by the alkali industry was raised in parliament. Since the 1830s, the industry had been producing sodium carbonate (used in making soap, glass and textiles) and giving off hundreds of tonnes of gaseous hydrochloric acid. *The Times* noted that whole tracts of countryside had been "swept by deadly blights till they are as barren as the shores of the Dead Sea".[6] In 1863, the world's first broad-ranging pollution control law – the Alkali Act – was passed, finally confirming a growing belief that central government should do something about controlling air pollution.[7] The Act created the Alkali Inspectorate, the world's first government agency designed specifically to deal with an environmental problem. The first inspector was Dr Robert Angus Smith (1817–1884), a Scottish chemist living in Manchester.

During the 1850s and 1860s, Smith had made studies in and around Manchester, where he spotted a connection between coal-burning and local pollution. He identified three kinds of air: "that with carbonate of ammonia in the fields at a distance. . .that with sulphate of ammonia in the suburbs. . .and that with sulphuric acid, or acid sulphate, in the town".[8] In his seminal book *Air and Rain: The Beginnings of a Chemical Climatology*, published in 1872, he outlined the process of acidification, coined the term "acid rain", and described the connection between the burning of coal, wind direction, corrosion and acid damage to vegetation. Smith's findings and conclusions have stood the test of time, but his work was largely overlooked until 1981, when his analysis was developed for a report by the US National Academy of Sciences.[9]

At the time that Smith was working in Manchester, London was beginning to gain a notoriety for smogs which it has yet to live down. (The word "smog" – an amalgam of "smoke" and "fog" – was invented in the nineteenth century to describe London's pollution.) Days or weeks of continuous fog repeatedly pushed up local rates of death from respiratory problems. A fog in December 1873 resulted in 500 deaths, and a three-week fog in February 1880 in more than 2,000 deaths.[10] Industrial pollution was part of the problem, but the main culprit was domestic smoke. In 1880 it was estimated that nearly 600,000 homes in London had more than 3.5 million fireplaces, almost all of them burning coal.[11] In 1880, Rollo Russell, son of Prime Minister Lord John Russell, published his book *London Fogs*, and launched a campaign aimed at drawing attention to the dangers of the fogs. He speculated that they were damaging fabrics and buildings, reducing by a third the amount of sunlight London received, depressing property values, and causing damage worth £5.2 million annually.

The United Kingdom's early awareness of pollution followed its early industrialization, but even in other, less industrialized parts of Europe, the more percipient observers of the environment were beginning to worry about the effects of smoke from coal. As early as 1727, the Swedish botanist Carl Von Linné described the sulphur given off by a 500-year-old smelter at Falun, north-west of Stockholm. The smelter, he wrote, gave off "a poisonous, pungent sulphur smoke, poisoning the air wide around. . .corrod[ing] the earth so that no herbs can grow around it."[12] In 1881, a Norwegian scientist observed polluted snowfall and attributed it to a large town or industrial district in the United Kingdom.[13] Just before the first world war, mass deaths began to occur among salmon in the rivers of southern Norway. Lakes, too, began losing their fish. Since 1970, no salmon have been caught in the region, and two-thirds of the lakes have lost their brown trout stocks. But it was only in the 1950s that the link with acid rain was established.

Research in the United Kingdom and Austria from 1911 to 1919 showed that natural rain and dilute sulphuric acid inhibited plant growth, and that atmospheric deposition of substances accelerated the acidification of forest soils.[14] In Canada, in the late nineteenth-century, open-bed roasting of high-sulphur copper ores destroyed vegetation in the vicinity of Sudbury, Ontario, and ruined crops in neighbouring farms (see chapter 7). By 1916 the farmers were agreed that action was needed, but instead of dealing with the source of the pollution, the government merely declared local areas unfit for

cultivation. In 1924 a farmer from Manchester sued the power station at Barton for compensation, arguing that its sulphur emissions
were damaging his crops. His claim was rejected by the House of
Lords, but the case generated considerable public debate.

Post-war research

During and after the second world war, the Swedish scientist Hans
Egnér began a systematic study of how vegetation could receive
nutrients through the deposition of airborne substances, and in
1948 began the first large-scale precipitation chemistry network in
Europe.[15] This network was then expanded by Carl Gustav Rossby
into the European Air Chemistry Network, which has since provided
a continuing record of precipitation chemistry.[16]

Beginning in 1955, the Canadian ecologist Eville Gorham published a series of papers in which he argued that acid precipitation
could affect the buffering capacity of bedrock, soils and lakes.
Working in England, Gorham and a colleague found acid lakes
in Cheshire and acid pools in the Lake District, and noted that
acid rain fell in the Lake District whenever the winds blew from
urban industrial areas. His research established that: (1) much of
the acidity in precipitation near industrial regions could be attributed
to emissions from fossil fuel combustion; (2) acid precipitation was
linked to losses of alkalinity in surface water, and increases in the
acidity of bog waters and soils; and (3) there was a link between acid
precipitation and bronchitis in humans.

Swedish researchers – notably the atmospheric chemists Erik
Eriksson and Carl Gustav Rossby – now became convinced that
airborne pollutants could be dispersed and transformed in the
atmosphere, and carried and deposited at various distances from
their source. In the 1960s the Swedish scientist Svante Odén – a
colleague of Eriksson and Rossby – brought together existing knowledge about acid precipitation in the fields of limnology, agriculture
and atmospheric chemistry, and argued the link between industrial
emissions and environmental damage (largely to fish and lakes). The
Swedish daily newspaper *Dagens Nyheter* published a piece by Odén
in 1967, and public attention was captured for the first time. In 1968,
Odén published a paper in which he argued that precipitation over

Scandinavia was becoming increasingly acidic, and that large quantities of the sulphur compounds that caused the acidification came
from UK and central European industrial emissions.[17] In 1971–72,
Henning Rodhe and his colleagues showed that sulphur pollutants
could be carried 1,000 km (600 miles) or more.[18] Acid pollution
had finally become a public issue.

The formation of acids

Since these early discoveries, the science of acid pollution has
made rapid progress. How acids are formed in the atmosphere
is increasingly better understood, and there is some scientific
consensus emerging over the relationship between pollutive emissions and acid deposition. But there is less agreement about how
acid actually damages plants, trees, crops, lakes, fish, buildings and
people. How much of the damage is due to acid pollution, and how
much to other factors, is still hotly debated. The unanswered questions in turn continued to be used throughout the 1970s and 1980s
as an argument by policy-makers opposed to "precipitate" action to
control acid pollution. They typically argue that the "hhuge acid rain
research effort provides ample data showing that the link between
SO_2 emissions and the acidity of rain is far weaker than generally
supposed, and...that the link between acid rain and ecological
damage is even weaker, or nearly nonexistent".[19]

Briefly, the acid rain debate hinges around the argument
that sulphur dioxide (SO_2), nitrogen oxides (NO_x), hydrocarbons
(HC) and particulates given off by power plants, industry and
vehicles can be converted into sulphuric and nitric acids in the
atmosphere, on the surface of buildings, inside plants, or below
ground, into sulphuric and nitric acids. Depending on a variety of
biological, chemical and meteorological factors, soils, forests, lakes,
rivers, animal and plant life, and buildings are susceptible in varying
degrees to the effects of these pollutants, acting alone or in tandem
with other factors. HC and NO_x can also combine (especially in
summer sunlight) to form ozone (O_3), another persistent and damaging pollutant.

There are three main links in the acid pollution chain: emission,
transport and transformation, and deposition.

Emission: what goes up must come down

All plants and animals contain some sulphur absorbed from their environment. Several hundred million years ago, fossil fuels were formed when dead animals and plants decomposed and were broken down into liquids (oil), gases (natural gas) and solids (coal and peat). In the same swamps and sediments, mineral sulphides (pyrites) were formed, probably by bacteria.

When fossil fuels are burned, or sulphide ores are smelted (roasted) to extract metal, the long-stored sulphur is released as SO_2. The sulphur content of oil and coal varies, depending largely on where it comes from. Crude oil can have anything from 0.1% to 3% sulphur content, staying roughly uniform according to the geographical location of the oil. Coal can have a sulphur content of anything from 0.48% to 5%, but is by no means uniform according to source; sulphur content varies from one grade to the next, and even from one seam to the next in the same mine, reflecting local variations in ecological conditions millions of years ago. Hard coals (like anthracite) are normally low in sulphur, while soft coals (bituminous, sub-bituminous and lignite/brown) can be much higher. But there are exceptions: while most soft UK and southern Brazilian coal has a sulphur content of up to 3%, most of the soft brown coal mined in West Germany's Rhineland has a sulphur content of less than 1%.[20]

Averaged over the globe, more than half the acidity of rain, snow and fog may be due to natural sources (such as SO_2 from volcanoes, and NO_x from chemical and bacterial nitrification in soil),[21] but about 120 million tonnes of SO_2 are emitted every year from coal- or oil-fired power stations, industries that use fossil fuels, and metal smelting. The geographical concentration of non-natural SO_2 varies, with the highest levels in the industrial centres of Europe, North America and south-east Asia. In Europe, about 90% of atmospheric SO_2 is thought to be non-natural.[22] In the United States, while total SO_2 emissions increased between 1960 and 1970, pollution control led to decreases in urban concentrations.[23]

In the United Kingdom and the United States, coal-fired power stations account for two-thirds of non-natural SO_2 emissions. In West Germany they account for half. In Canada, smelters account

Table 1.1: Annual SO$_2$ emissions (in thousand tonnes) and deposition (%)

	1980[2]	Most recent figure[3]	Sulphur deposition[1] Foreign	Domestic	Undecided
USSR[4]	25 000	24 000	32	53	15
USA	23 200	20 800			
China	–	18 000[5]	–	90	10[6]
Poland	4 100	4 300	52	42	6
East Germany	4 000	4 000	32	65	3
Canada	4 650	3 727	c50	50	–
UK	4 670	3 540	12	79	9
Spain	3 250	3 250	18	63	19
Italy	3 800	3 150	22	70	8
India	3 200[7]	–	–	100[6]	–
Czechoslovakia	3 100	3 050	56	37	7
West Germany	3 200	2 400	45	48	7
France	3 558	1 845	32	54	14
Yugoslavia	1 175	1 800	41	51	8
Hungary	1 633	1 420	52	42	4
Bulgaria*	1 034	1 140	–	–	–
South Africa[6]	1 000	–	–	100	–
Greece	800	720	–	–	–
Belgium	799	467	–	–	–
Finland	584	370	55	26	19
Denmark	438	326	–	–	–
Netherlands	487	315	–	–	–
Portugal	266	305	–	–	–
Turkey	–	276	–	–	–
Sweden	483	272	58	18	24
Austria	354	170	–	–	–
Ireland	219	138	–	–	–
Romania	200	–	–	–	–
Norway	141	100†	63	8	29
Switzerland	126	63	–	–	–
Luxembourg	23	13	–	–	–
EC total	21 510	16 469	–	–	–

World total   Approx 120 million tonnes in 1980[6]

* = Estimate † = preliminary

Sources: 1. EMEP and UNECE (except where indicated).

2,3. From United Nations, *National Strategies and Policies for Air Pollution Abatement* (New York: United Nations, 1987) (except where indicated). These are the most recent available figures. Those in column 3 come from the years between 1983 and 1986, so although not directly comparative, they give a good general idea of changes in emissions.

4. UNECE figures, 1982.

5. Ross, Lester, *Environmental Policy in China* (Bloomington: Indiana University Press, 1988).

6. Author's estimate.

7. Centre for Science and Environment, India, 1985.

for 63% of emissions. The largest single source of non-natural SO_2 in the world is the copper and nickel smelting complex at Sudbury, Ontario, which annually produced 632,000 tones of SO_2 in the early 1980s (about the same as the whole of Sweden and Finland combined). The Sudbury nickel smelter alone is estimated to have emitted more SO_2 in the period 1969–79 than all the volcanoes in the history of the earth.[24] SO_2 emissions in Europe probably doubled between 1950 and 1973 and peaked between 1975 and 1978. Since about 1980, they have fallen in most countries, by between 2% (Czechoslovakia) and 52% (Austria). Emissions in the United States rose from about 12 million tonnes in 1950 to about 24 million tonnes in 1965, and stabilized at that level before falling off between 1980 and 1983 to 20.8 million tonnes. In Canada more than 3.7 million tonnes are emitted yearly, a 17% fall since the mid-1950s. China – with annual estimated emissions of 18 million tonnes[25] – is the third largest source of SO_2 after the Soviet Union and the United States.

Burning fossil fuel is also the main source of non-natural NO_x, the second key element in acid pollution. Combustion oxidizes both the nitrogen in fuel and some of the nitrogen naturally present in the air (which is 80% nitrogen). The quantity and composition of the nitrogen oxides depends on how combustion is performed and at what temperatures. Burning will normally oxidize 5–40% of the nitrogen in coal, 40–50% of that in heavy oil, and nearly 100% of that in light oil and gas. The higher the temperature, the more nitrogen oxides are formed. Power stations which burn fossil fuels are the major source of NO_x in industrialized countries, but road traffic makes a big contribution, especially in larger cities.

Not all countries can provide detailed information on their NO_x emissions, but in Western Europe about 30–50% of the emissions come from motor vehicles, and another 30–40% from power plants, mainly coal-fired. (In Sweden, about 30–40% of non-natural atmospheric nitrogen compounds come from agriculture and forestry, both of which use much nitrate-based fertilizer. Anything from 10% to 75% of the nitrate can evaporate, depending on conditions when the fertilizer is spread.) In 1980, 44% of NO_x emissions in the United States and 61% in Canada came from road transport.[26] Eastern Europe has lower NO_x emissions, but it

Table 1.2: Annual NO_x emissions (in thousand tonnes)

	1980	Most recent figure
United States	20 300	19 400
West Germany	3 100	2 900
USSR[1]	2 790	2 930
UK	1 916	1 690
France[2]	1 867	1 693
Canada	1 725	1 785
Italy[3]	1 550	1 537
Czechoslovakia	1 204	1 100
Spain[4]	–	1 122
Poland	–	840
Netherlands	535	522
Belgium	442	385
Sweden	328	305
Hungary[3]	–	300
Finland	280	250
Denmark	251	238
Austria	216	216
Norway[3]	–	215
Switzerland	196	187
Portugal	166	192
Bulgaria (est)	–	150
Greece	127	150
Ireland	67	68
Luxembourg	23	22

No figures available for East Germany, Romania, Turkey, Yugoslavia.

1. Figures for European USSR only; total figures for USSR certainly much higher – probably close to US figures.
2. Does not include 700,000 tonnes from agricultural activities.
3. Preliminary figures.
4. Figures represent upper limit of emissions.

Source: United Nations, *National Strategies and Policies for Air Pollution Abatement* (New York: United Nations, 1987). Figures under second column come from the period 1983–1986.

also has fewer cars than the West, and the types of vehicles and the quality of roads (which affect speeds, and therefore emissions) differ. In the Third World, vehicles are usually the main source of NO_x.

Because there has been no systematic monitoring of NO_x emissions, it is more difficult to give exact figures on present and future levels. As with SO_2, about half the NO_x in the earth's atmosphere is non-natural, but again the proportion is much greater in the industrialized countries. In Europe and North America, non-natural NO_x outweighs natural NO_x by 5–10 times.[27] The proportion of NO_x in the atmosphere in Europe is thought to have grown by 40–50% during the 1970s, but rates vary.[28] In some countries, such as West Germany, the United Kingdom and France, NO_x emissions are falling (see Table 1.2). In others, such as the Soviet Union, Canada and Greece, they are on the rise. The United States is the world's biggest producer of NO_x – about 19.4 million tonnes in 1983.

NO_x is a critical factor in many Third World cities, where a combination of heavy road traffic and local wind patterns can often recirculate nitrogen oxides and other pollutants, creating severe photochemical smog. Air pollutants from road traffic is all too common in large cities throughout Latin America and Asia. The still and stable air over many south-east Asian cities creates ideal conditions for the build-up of pollutants from road traffic and industry (see chapter 9).

Transport and transformation

Once in the atmosphere, SO_2 and NO_x can undergo complex chemical processes that can transform them into sulphuric acid (H_2SO_4) and nitric acid (HNO_3). The transport of pollutants, the amount of acid produced, and the effect of acid pollutants depends on many different factors, such as weather conditions (wind, cloud cover, humidity and sunlight); the presence of other pollutants; the height at which pollutants are released, and the length of time the pollutants remain in the atmosphere. Difficulties in measuring long-range transport patterns have been a key factor in the debate about the causes and effects of acid pollution.

Measuring acidity

Acids are chemical substances which, in a water solution, release positively charged hydrogen ions. Sulphuric acid consists of sulphate and hydrogen ions, and nitric acid of nitrate and hydrogen ions. The acidity or alkalinity of a solution is determined by the percentage of hydrogen ions that the solution contains, measured on the potential hydrogen (pH) scale (see Figure 1.1). This ranges from 0 to 14, with 0 being the most acid (battery acid has a pH of 1), 7 being neutral (the pH of distilled water) and 14 the most alkaline (a saturated solution of ammonia in water has a pH of 11). The scale is logarithmic, which means that a step of a single number increases or decreases acidity by a factor of 10. So a solution with a pH of 6 is ten times more acidic than one with a pH of 7, and a solution with a pH of 5 is 100 times more acidic.

All rain is slightly acidic because of the natural carbon dioxide (CO_2) content of air. Dissolved in water, CO_2 forms carbonic acid, a weak acid. So while distilled pure water has a pH of 7, normal or unpolluted rainwater (water in equilibrium with atmospheric carbon dioxide) has a pH of about 5.6, although the presence of naturally occurring SO_2, ammonia, organic compounds or dust can cause normal pH values of between 4.9 and 6.5.[29] Some acid in rainwater is useful in helping water dissolve soil minerals, releasing them for

Figure 1.1: The pH scale

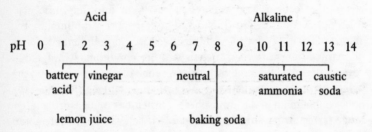

Figure 1.2: Acidity of European precipitation, 1985 (pH units)

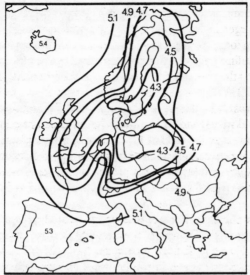

Source: Co-operative Program for Monitoring and Evaluation of the
            Long-Range Transmission of Air Pollutants in Europe, Nor-
            wegian Institute for Air Research, Lillestrom, 1987.

Figure 1.3: Acidity of North American precipitation, 1985 (pH units)

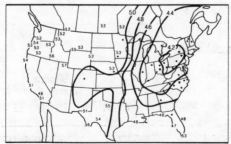

Source: A.R. Olsen, Pacific Northwest Laboratory, Richland, Washington,
            1987.

Note: ● = station showing no trend in acidity, 1979–84
            ▼ = station showing decreasing acidity, 1979–84

plants and animals. Acidity is often neutralized by the soil itself, for example by the alkaline carbonates in limestone. But higher levels of acidity can become destructive. Rainwater during a storm in Pitlochry, Scotland, in April 1974 had a pH of 2.4 – similar to lemon juice.[30] An even lower pH value was unofficially recorded in rain during a 1978 storm in Wheeling, West Virginia, when the pH of the rain fell below 2.0, making it more acid than lemon juice.[31]

Some water and soils are naturally acid. Small pools in upland bogs of sphagnum (a species of moss found in swamps and fens) commonly have a pH of 3–4, but only a fraction of this can be blamed on pollution. There are some larger naturally acidic lakes in Sweden with a pH of 4.5, but they are exceptions to the rule. Surface water (lakes, streams, seas) normally has a pH of 6–9. Lakes in areas with bedrocks that do not weather easily or where the surrounding soils are low in lime content can have a "natural" pH of 6. Such lakes are also low in nutrients. In favourable summer conditions, the pH of nutrient-rich lakes in lime-rich areas can be as high as 9.

Dry and wet phase reactions

There are two phases involved in the formation of acids: dry and wet. In both, SO_2 and NO_x are converted to sulphate and nitrate. Dry or "gas phase" conversion predominates in the vicinity of emission sources, and wet or "aqueous phase" conversion, involving reactions within water droplets, is more predominant at a greater distance. Gas phase SO_2, NO_x, sulphates and nitrates return to earth in the form of gases and particles, especially in the vicinity of the sources of pollution (within 300 km/190 miles). This is known as dry deposition. The rest of the oxides, converted to acids by aqueous phase reactions, can be carried as far as 1000 km (600 miles), eventually returning to earth as acid rain, snow, sleet or fog. This is known as wet deposition.

In the gas phase, oxides can be converted to acid in many different ways, usually through reactions with excited molecules, atoms and free radicals (atoms containing one or more unpaired electrons: they exist for only a brief period of time before reaction to produce a stable molecule). Because these radicals are formed under the influence of sunlight, sunny weather encourages conversion to acid, and the rate of conversion falls off rapidly after sunset. In the gas phase, the most important intermediate for converting SO_2 and NO_x to H_2SO_4 and HNO_3 seems to be the hydroxy radical (HO).[32]

HO itself can be formed in several ways, the most common being via a complex reaction involving ozone. Where the air temperature is greater than 15°C (59°F), the NO_x and unburned HC in vehicle exhaust gases can react in prolonged strong sunlight to form ozone, an unstable form of oxygen containing three instead of two atoms per molecule. NO_x plays a part in the formation of ozone, which is in turn involved in the conversion of sulphur and nitrogen oxides to acids. When ozone breaks down, excited oxygen atoms are released and may react with water to produce HO. The rates at which the acids are formed is thought to depend on the concentrations of HO present. Direct measurement of HO in the atmosphere is difficult, but the US National Research Council has estimated the rates of conversion of SO_2 and NO_2 respectively at 16.4% and 150% per day on polluted sunny summer days (when HO concentrations are high) and 3% and 25% per day on polluted sunny winter days (when the concentrations are lower).[33]

Until recently, relatively little attention was paid to the role of ozone in air pollution, beyond its well-known and well-documented effects during photochemical smogs in urban areas. But the formation of non-natural ozone has increased with the rising levels of NO_x in the atmosphere, and ozone is now recognized as a primary factor in the formation of acid pollution, and even as the cause of damage wrongly blamed on acid pollution. This low-altitude non-natural ozone should not be confused with the natural ozone in the stratosphere, which forms a thin, protective layer 7–16 km (4.5–10 miles) above the earth's surface, preventing damaging ultra-violet radiation from reaching the surface. This natural ozone is currently under assault from a different quarter – the chlorofluorocarbons used in refrigerants, aerosol propellants, and packaging.

Ozone damage to trees has been recorded in the United States since the 1940s,[34] and there is definite evidence that it can damage sensitive vegetation in rural areas of Europe.[35] It may also damage human health and property. While SO_2 emissions in West Germany remained relatively stable in the period 1966–78, NO_x emissions grew by 50%, leading three UK scientists to suggest that ozone may well have been the prime cause of forest decline at that time.[36] Scientists at Imperial College, London have been studying the effects of ozone on crops since 1977, and believe that it can reduce yields by 10–20% in sensitive species. Laboratory findings have been supported by evidence of crop damage in open fields. The team says that ozone concentrations sufficient to damage crops can be expected to occur intermittently over most of the British Isles in years when hours of sunshine are low.[37]

In dry deposition, pollutants can return to earth as oxides and be converted to acid through adsorption (where a gas accumulates on the surface of a solid) or absorption (where SO_2 and NO_x can enter the stomata – the leaf pores that control the passage of gases into and out of a plant – and be oxidized to acid inside the leaf). Acids can also be formed directly on the surface of vegetation or on the ground when dry-deposited material is dissolved in rain or snow. Dry deposition is the simplest form of acid pollution, but is still not completely understood; deposition rates are difficult to measure, and the pathways for the transport of dry pollutants and the nature of reactions on surfaces are unclear. Roughly a third of sulphur emissions from the north-eastern United States are thought to be dry deposited.[38] The oxides in industrial emissions, particularly those in hot gases given off by smelters or power plants, can rise to altitudes of several hundred metres. At that height, the average wind speed is about 36 kph (22 mph) – fast enough to cover the distance from Pittsburgh (United States) to Quebec (Canada) in 24 hours, or London (United Kingdom) to Gothenburg (Sweden) in 36 hours.

The longer the pollutants stay in the atmosphere, the greater the proportion converted to acid sulphate and nitrate. The time they are airborne and the distance they are carried depends on several factors, from the height of the smokestacks to wind and weather conditions. With a strong wind, the oxides and acids can stay in the atmosphere for several days and be carried several hundred kilometres. Because the prevailing winds in Europe and North America blow from the south/south-west to the north/north-east, the major routes of airborne pollution are from western and central Europe to Scandinavia, from eastern Europe to the Soviet

Union, and from the United States to Canada. Winds also carry pollution across the United States-Mexican border (both ways), and from China to Japan.

In the aqueous phase reaction, which is much better understood than the gas phase (but is still open to some dispute), SO_2 and water can turn to acid in as little as an hour. The formation of sulphuric and nitric acids in liquid aerosols, cloud droplets, and precipitation depends on gas phase reactions to provide the necessary reactants.[39] Because the presence of water vapour is obviously essential, oxidation on a cloudy day will be more rapid than on a clear day. Hydrogen peroxide (H_2O_2) and ozone are thought to be the two main agents involved in oxidizing water-dissolved sulphur into sulphuric acid. Other paths may involve HO, Nozone, soot, or ions of manganese and iron.[40] Pollutants can attach themselves to water droplets in several different ways. The most important of these is nucleation, where water molecules condense into suitable receptors, such as dust and other pollutants, forming a cloud of droplets or ice crystals containing the pollutant. The second major process – diffusion – results froom the diffusion of pollutant particles through the air to the surface of a water droplets. Finally, pollutants and droplets can become attached by simple inertia, where falling particles become attached to the droplets.[41] Much less is known about the aqueous phase formation of nitric acid, but ozone is certainly sometimes involved.

The linearity debate

One of the most contentious issues in the acid pollution debate is the question of linearity. Is there a linear relationship between emissions and deposition? In other words, will a given reduction in emissions result in a time proportional reduction in deposition? Opponents of action to curb acid pollution often argue that the formation of acid depends so much on weather conditions that emissions do not always convert to acids, and so reducing emissions may not reduce acid pollution proportionately. In its 1982–83 annual report, the UK's Central Electricity Generating Board concluded that "the acidity of rain in Europe cannot be expected to respond proportionately to changes in the amount of sulphur dioxide emitted".[42]

The earliest research into acid deposition tended to assume a linear relationship. Then evidence emerged in the early 1980s that the amount of acid formed depended more on photochemical oxidants, such as ozone, than on SO_2 levels. The suggestion was that once these oxidants had been exhausted, no more acid could be formed. Hence it could logically be argued that a reduction in levels of NO_x and HC (which create the oxidants) would have more effect on reducing acid pollution than a reduction in SO_2 levels.[43] In 1983, the US National Research Council (NRC) concluded that there was no evidence to support a strongly non-linear relationship in north-western North America, when emission and deposition figures were averaged out over a year and over the entire area. "If the emissions of sulphur dioxide from all sources in this region were reduced by the same fraction, the result would be a corresponding fractional reduction in deposition."[44]

On the other hand, the NRC pointed out that in Europe, where precipitation monitoring programmes had been in existence for much longer, there was some direct evidence of a non-linear relationship. For example, monitoring between 1960 and 1975 found constant or declining rates of sulphate deposition despite the fact that there were significant increases in SO_2 emissions in the same period. But there were some doubts about the sampling and the analytical techniques used. Several papers published since then have challenged the idea of non-linearity in Europe. A UK study showed UK SO_2 emissions and rainfall acidity falling in 1974–82,[45] and studies in Sweden and Norway have added further support to the linearity argument.[46]

Further evidence of linearity in the United States came in a 1984 study by the Environmental Defense Fund (EDF) in the south-western United States. Using information from south-western copper smelters and data from the monitoring stations of the National Acid Deposition Program, which makes daily measurements of pollution, the EDF was able to determine fluctuations in acid deposition. These were then compared with smelter emission figures. Acid pollution was worst on days of heavy smelter activity, and reduced on days when the smelters were operating at lower production levels. The report concluded: "The variations in sulphur concentrations at all monitoring stations are consistent with the variations in smelter emissions."[47]

Deposition

The environmental effects of acid deposition depend on whether it is dry or wet, on the level of contact it has with plants, watercourses and buildings, and on local environmental and meteorological conditions. The National Research Council identifies three levels of receptors of acid pollution:

- Primary receptors come into direct contact with atmospheric pollutants, for example the surfaces of buildings, trees, plants and unprotected soil.
- Secondary receptors come into contact with pollutants only after they have been in contact with other materials, for example the inner foliage of plants or the soil beneath vegetation.
- Tertiary receptors are indirectly affected by pollutants, for example subsoil, bedrock, and watercourses and lakes that receive most of their water from runoff.[48]

Dry deposition has several direct effects on the environment. It can attack and corrode buildings, metals, stone and even leather, paper and textiles. It can be deposited on forests and farmland, affecting plant growth and crop yields. It can mix with fog and dust to create smogs that can cause respiratory problems among susceptible people and animals.

Wet deposition has both direct and indirect effects. It can increase the acidity of lakes and rivers, which is made worse by the inflow of acids and metals from adjacent soils. It is implicated in the death of aquatic species, making lakes and rivers too barren to support fish life. It can cause metals such as aluminium, cadmium and mercury to be carried into soil water, groundwater, lakes and streams, depleting the stock of nutrients in the soils and weakening plants. It has been implicated in reduced crop yields and the corrosion of buildings and structures. More controversially, it has been implicated in the aggravation of heart, lung and respiratory disease in humans – exactly how is still a matter of debate.

NOTES

1. Martin, W., "Legislative air pollution strategies in various countries", in *Clean Air* 9, 1975, pp. 28–32.
2. Evelyn, John, *Fumifugium: or the Inconvenience of the Aer and Smoake of London Dissipated*, reproduced in James P. Lodge, *The Smoake of London: Two Prophecies* (New York: Maxwell Reprint Comany, 1969).
3. Ashby, Eric and Mary Anderson, *The Politics of Clean Air* (Oxford: Clarendon Press, 1981).
4. *The Times*, 24 April 1845.
5. Ashby and Anderson, see note 3.
6. *The Times*, 12 May 1862.
7. Ashby and Anderson, see note 3.
8. Smith, Robert Angus, *Air and Rain: the Beginnings of a Chemical Climatology* (London: Longmans, Green & Co., 1872).
9. Cowling, Ellis B., "Acid precipitation in historical perspective", in *Environmental Science and Technology* 16:2, January 1982, pp. 110A–22A.
10. Ashby and Anderson, see note 3.
11. *The Times*, 5 November 1880.
12. Linné, 1734, quoted in Cowling, see note 9.
13. Brögger, W.C., 1881, quoted in Cowling, see note 9.
14. Cowling, see note 9.
15. Cowling, see note 9.
16. Emanuelsson, A., E. Eriksson, and Hans Egnér, 1954, quoted in Cowling, see note 9.
17. Odén, Svante, "The acidification of air and precipitation and its consequences in the natural environment". Ecology Committee Bulletin No. 1 (Stockholm: Swedish National Science Research Council, 1968).
18. Rodhe, Henning, P. Crutzen, F.R.G. Vanderpol, and A. Vanderpol, 1981, quoted in Cowling, see note 9.
19. Katzenstein, A.W., "Acid rain: a further look at the evidence", in *Power Engineering* 24, March 1986, pp. 32–6.
20. Figures from World Energy Conference.
21. National Research Council, *Acid Deposition: Atmospheric Processes in Eastern North America* (Washington, DC: National Academy Press, 1983).
22. Overrein, Lars, "The European acid rain situation", in *Ecological Effects of Acid Deposition* (Solna, Sweden : National Swedish Environmental Protection Board), Report PM 1636, SOLNA 1983.
23. Altschuller, A.P., "Seasonal and episodic trends in sulfate concentrations (1963–1978) in the eastern United States", in *Environmental Science and Technology* 14, 1980, pp. 1337–48.

24. Altschuller, A.P. and G.A. McBean, *The LRTAP Problem in North America: A Preliminary Overview* (US–Canada Research Consulation Group on Long Range Transport of Air Pollutants, 1979).

25. Ross, Lester, *Environmental Policy in China* (Bloomington: Indiana University Press, 1988).

26. Gould, Roy, *Going Sour: Science and Politics of Acid Rain* (Boston: Birkäuser, 1985).

27. Galloway, James N. and Peter J. Dillon, *Effects of Acid Deposition: The Importance of Nitrogen* (Stockholm: Ministry of Agriculture, Stockholm Conference on the Acidification of the Environment, 1982).

28. Grennefelt, Peringe, *Oxidised Nitrogen Compounds in Long Range Transported Air Masses* (Stockholm: Swedish Water and Air Pollution Institute, 1979); and Brimblecombe, P. and D.H. Stedman, "Historical evidence for a dramatic increase in the nitrate component of acid rain", in *Nature* 298, May 1982, pp. 460–62.

29. Charlson, R.J. and Henning Rodhe, "Factors controlling the acidity of natural rainwater", in *Nature* 295, February 1982, pp.683–5; and Galloway, James N., G.E. Likens, W.C. Keene, and J.M. Miller, "The composition of precipitation in remote areas of the world", in *Journal of Geophysical Resources* 11, October 1982, pp. 8771–86.

30. Environment Canada, *Downwind: The Acid Rain Story* (Ottawa: Ministry of Supply and Services, Canada, 1982).

31. Eckholm, Erik, *Down to Earth* (London: Pluto Press, 1982).

32. National Research Council, see note 21.

33. National Research Council, see note 21.

34. Ulrich, Bernhard, "An ecosystem oriented hypothesis on the effect of air pollution on forest ecosystems", in National Swedish Environmental Protection Board, *Ecological Effects of Acid Deposition* Report PM 1636, SOLNA 1983.

35. Ashmore, Mike, "Effects of ozone on vegetation in the United Kingdom", in Peringe Grennefelt, (ed.), *The Evaluation and Assessment of the Effects of Photochemical Oxidants on Human Health, Agricultural Crops, Forestry, Materials and Visibility* (Göteborg: Swedish Environmental Research Institute, 1984), pp. 92–104; and Lena Skärby, and Gun Sellden, "The effects of ozone on crops and forests", in *Ambio* 13:2, 1984, pp. 68–72.

36. Ashmore, Mike, Nigel Bell and Jack Rutter, "The role of ozone in forest damage in West Germany", in *Ambio* 14:2, 1985, pp. 81–7.

37. *ENDS Report* 101, June 1983.

38. National Research Council, see note 21.

39. National Research Council, see note 21.

40. National Research Council, see note 21.
41. National Research Council, see note 21.
42. Central Electricity Generating Board, *Annual Report 1982/83* (London: CEGB, 1983).
43. Dudley, Nigel, Mark Barrett, and David Baldock, *The Acid Rain Controversy* (London: Earth Resources Research, 1985).
44. National Research Council, see note 21.
45. Harriman, R. and D.E. Wells, "Causes and effects of surface water acidification in Scotland". Paper to Annual Conference, Institute of Water Pollution Control, 1984.
46. *ENDS Report* 116, September 1984; and Richard F. Wright, and Arne Henriksen, "Regional survey of lakes and streams in southwestern Scotland", SNSF Report IR 72/80, April 1979.
47. Oppenheimer, Michael and Robert E. Yuhnke, *Sulfur Pollution: Strategy for Preventing Acid Pollution Damage in the Intermountain Air Shed* (Boulder, Colorado: Environmental Defense Fund, 1984).
48. National Research Council, see note 21.

2. Acid Damage

Acid pollution can damage trees, plants and crops. It can acidify soils, rivers and lakes, leading to a decline in freshwater animal and plant life. It can threaten human health, and corrode stone and metal, both above and below ground. But the mechanisms by which this damage occurs, and the relative contribution of the different components of acid pollution and other natural or non-natural factors, are still debated. Most of the research on recent forest damage in Europe has concentrated on the role of air pollution, but even here there is no certainty or agreement about exactly which pollutants are causing the damage, and how that damage is caused. This poses real problems not only for scientists, but for policy-makers. Without a full understanding of how the damage occurs, it is difficult to agree workable policy responses. It is even more difficult to convince government and industry that they should spend millions in pollution control when no-one knows for sure exactly which pollutants are causing the damage.

Forests: major declines all over Europe

Forests are complex ecosystems, a chain of interdependent ecological processes involving trees, soil, water, the air, climate and other living organisms. They are natural air filters; they enrich the air with humidity and regulate the local climate, and they control ground and surface water by collecting, storing, filtering and distributing it and regulating the water table. Forests bind soil and prevent erosion. They prevent landslides, rockfalls and avalanches, provide effective windbreaks, control the passage of air into otherwise vulnerable areas such as valley basins, and provide protection against frost. They support a complex community of wildlife: animals, birds, insects, and plants. Forests are also a major economic resource.

This essential resource is now under widespread and virulent attack from acid pollution. All over Europe, previously healthy stands of forest are dead or dying. Although isolated pockets of damage have long been evident, the more widespread decline has been recent and rapid, the end product of decades of acidification. A mysterious disease was noticed in white fir trees north of the Alps as early as the eighteenth century, but it was only in 1970 that this *Tannensterben* (tree death) took on a new intensity. The first real signs of a widespread problem came in the late 1970s, especially after the 1976 drought. The implications for West German forestry took a new and more sombre turn in 1979, with the discovery of a disease affecting Norway spruce, a species that covers 40% of the country.[1] Suggestions of a link between forest damage and acid pollution were initially met with scepticism; for some, dieback was a temporary phenomenon, attributable as much as anything to climatic stress. But symptoms similar to those in German fir and spruce were subsequently found in spruce forests right across central Europe and Scandinavia, and then in Scots pine and European beech forests.

By 1982, the West German government was sufficiently alarmed about forest decline to finally agree to SO_2 emission controls (see chapter 6). About 8% of German forests were then affected by *Waldsterben* (forest death); by 1983 the proportion had grown to 34%, and by 1984 to about 50%.[2] By 1985, almost every species of forest tree in Europe was affected, with damage evident on more than 5 million hectares (12 million acres) of forest in just four European countries: West Germany, Poland, Yugoslavia, and Czechoslovakia. Forest damage had also been found in East Germany, the Netherlands, Switzerland, France, Austria, Sweden and the United States. Foresters were shocked by the speed and breadth of the damage. By 1986, 87% of West Germany's firs were damaged, two-thirds of them seriously.[3]

In 1987, a UN report revealed that the United Kingdom – where scepticism about acid damage to forests has been greatest – had one of the highest percentages of damaged forests in Europe; two-thirds of UK conifers exhibited slight to severe damage.[4]

Waldsterben produces decreased or abnormal tree growth, or water stress. Most familiar forest diseases are caused by fungi, bacteria, insects, viruses and other pathogens, but the symptoms of *Waldsterben* suggested something altogether different. They included (in conifers) a yellowing and loss of needles, stunted growth, thinning out of tree tops, soft-rot and root damage; (in deciduous trees) discoloured and misshapen leaves, early leaf fall, dead tree tops, damaged bark, a lack of natural regrowth, and loss of resistance to disease and to other stresses such as storms or drought. Other symptoms included the loss of feeder roots, narrower tree rings, the death of herbaceous vegetation beneath, and – in the worst cases – death.[5] These symptoms have been found to varying degrees and in different combinations.

Despite all this damage, the precise links between forest dieback and acid pollution are still unclear. A European Commission report argued as recently as 1983 that there was "no unequivocal evidence" of acid deposition having affected the growth of trees in EC member states.[6] But in March of the same year, a council of environmental advisors to the West German government argued that all serious attempts to explain forest damage led inexorably to the conclusion that air pollutants, either alone or in combination with other pollutants and/or factors such as climate, location, pests, or forest cultivation influences, played "a decisive part in both causing the damage and determining its extent."[7]

In 1985, Peter Schütt of the University of Munich and Ellis Cowling of North Carolina State University listed some peculiar features of *Waldsterben*:

○ The visible symptoms started at about the same time in different parts of Europe, and within four years were found over large parts of the continent.
○ The disease affected almost every tree species (native and exotic) in central Europe, as well as various species of shrubs and herbs.
○ The disease occurred with similar intensity on soils that were rich or poor, acid or basic, wet or dry, and irrespective of climatic conditions, the direction of the slope in hilly or mountainous areas, or differences in forest management techniques.
○ Symptoms were generally (but not exclusively) worse on older trees and trees at higher altitudes.[8]

In all, 186 different hypotheses have emerged on forest damage,[9] involving problems like climatic stress (for example drought, frost, strong winds and storms), slow changes in the soil, the indiscriminate planting of trees at the turn of the century, and attacks by pests and diseases. Despite all the debate, four main points of agreement have emerged: (1) *Waldsterben* must be understood as a disease syndrome caused by several different primary and secondary factors; (2) the primary causes are none of the usual forest pathogens or diseases; (3) climatic extremes like drought or frost probably play only a secondary role; (4) air pollution is the primary cause. Whether damage begins in the leaves and needles and works down, or whether it begins in the roots and soil and works up, is a matter of some contention.

Interestingly, the typical symptoms of SO_2 damage (such as bleached leaves on deciduous trees, and red-brown needles on conifers) have not been found in West German forests except in connection with identifiable point sources; hence SO_2 damage in central Europe may be due more to stress brought on by low doses over long periods.[10] With research on *Waldsterben* in Europe now concentrating almost exclusively on air pollution, several schools of thought have emerged on the causes of forest death.

Soil acidification and aluminium toxicity
Developed in 1979 by Dr Bernhard Ulrich and his colleagues at the University of Göttingen in West Germany,[11] this theory argues that the natural acidification of forest soils is accelerated by acid deposition, which increases the concentration of soluble aluminium ions. The fine roots of trees are attacked, preventing them from taking up enough nutrients or water to survive.[12] Shortages of magnesium and calcium are particularly critical. Once the roots are damaged, the rest of the tree suffers. Recent evidence that forest decline follows dry summers (when soils become more acid and nutrients more scarce) lends credence to this theory.

Ozone injury
This is advocated by, among others, Dr Bernhard Prinz of the Landesanstalt für Immissionsschutz in Essen, West Germany.

There is still only limited direct evidence for ozone injury,[13] but it fits with the fact that SO_2 emissions in West Germany have decreased while NO_x emissions have increased.[14] Laboratory experiments have found sensitive species of pine being visibly damaged by low doses of ozone (O_3) within a matter of hours.[15] The ozone damages the surface of the needles, and acid mists or rain wash out nutrients like magnesium. Field experiments in the eastern United States and south-eastern England found ozone damage on, among others, species of birch and ash, but not on beech or oak.[16] In Hungary, though, ozone has been implicated in damage to oaks. The head of the Hungarian Forestry Department suggests that ozone causes oaks to dry out, and die from the top down.[17]

Ozone has also been implicated in the death of pine trees in the San Bernardino National Forest east of Los Angeles, a city notorious for its smogs. As early as 1969 it was revealed that 1.3 million ponderosa and Jeffrey pines had been affected. In areas where the highest ozone doses were measured, the timber yield of 30-year-old pines declined by 83%. Weakened trees were later attacked by bark beetles. Similar damage appeared in the Appalachian mountains of the eastern United States, but it was impossible to say with certainty whether ozone rather than a combination of pollutants was responsible.

Magnesium deficiency

Advanced particularly by Professor Karl Rehfuess of the University of Munich, this theory argues that acid deposition may add nitrogen to soil while leaching out magnesium and calcium from needles and soils.[18] The loss of magnesium may account for the yellowing of spruce needles commonly seen in West Germany, since magnesium plays a cental part in the structure of the chlorophyll molecule. The loss of magnesium and calcium from the leaves may cause the roots to work overtime to replace these crucial nutrients, and the resulting transfer of these nutrients from the soil increases the hydrogen:calcium ratio in the soil, and hence the acidity.

General stress
This hypothesis suggests that concentrations of SO_2, NO_x, oxidants, hydrocarbons (HC) and heavy metals are too small individually to cause damage. Combined, though, they could decrease the production of carbohydrates in plant leaves, thereby decreasing the vitality of roots and leaves. This lowers root production, reducing the ability of trees to withstand attacks from fungi, bacteria, viruses and insects, and making them more susceptible to the stresses of drought, frost and wind.[19]

Excess nutrients or nitrogen
This argues that forest ecosystems have been receiving excessive doses of sixteen elements considered essential for plant growth. The deposition of nitrogen in particular has been growing, encouraging increased growth and hence excessive demand for nutrients. Nutrient shortages in turn lead to an increased susceptibility to frost and root-disease fungi, changes in root:shoot ratio, and possible nitrogen fixation.

The ammonium hypothesis
This was put forward by Dr Bengt Nihlgard of the University of Lund in Sweden. Nitrogen in the form of ammonium or nitrate is an important plant nutrient, but most plants have adapted through evolution to be able to exist with very low levels of nitrogen. However acid deposition may build up nitrogen in soils and plants, leading to oversaturation. The nitrogen is transformed into ammonium, amines or amides. If tree growth is accelerated, trees may form large cells that are easily attacked by wind, drought and pests. The surplus nitrogen is transformed into ammonium, and this may be accompanied by oxidation and the release of hydrogen ions or organic acids. Soluble carbohydrates are consumed, non-protein nitrogen compounds and hydrogen ions are stored in leaves, root growth decreases and frost resistance is reduced. The result may be long-term tree damage.[20] Excess nitrogen may also saturate soils, contributing to soil acidification. This may help explain why good soils – which are already rich

in nitrogen and so will become saturated more quickly than poor soils
– are being acidified.

Heavy metal deposition

Fossil fuel combustion not only gives off SO_2 and NO_x, but also
heavy metals such as lead, cadmium, copper and zinc. Lead (given
off by leaded petrol) can not only directly inhibit root growth, but
mobile heavy metals can increase the leaching of nutrients. As
soil acidity increases, so does the mobility (and toxicity) of lead.
Potentially toxic levels of lead have been found in the mountains
of Vermont and North Carolina in the United States,[21] but similar
levels have yet to be found in West German forests.

Trees are more directly exposed to the influence of wind than
other plants. The particles, gases and acids they filter or screen
from the air may end up on their leaves or needles, their bark or on
the ground. Evergreens are more efficient at filtering than deciduous
trees, but this efficiency makes them more vulnerable to pollution:
because deciduous trees shed their leaves every year, the cycle of air

---

Table 2.1: Primary causes of forest decline (ranked in order of importance by region)

	W Europe	E Europe	N America
Ozone	1	2	1
Acid deposition	2	3	5
Other gaseous pollutants (eg SO_2 and NO_x)	3	1	3
Excess nitrogen deposition	4	–	2
Growth-altering organic chemicals	5	–	6
Heavy metals	–	4	4

Source: Hinrichsen, Don, 'Multiple pollutants and forest decline', in
Ambio 15:5, 1986, pp. 258–65.

pollution damage is temporarily broken. Some pollutants are swept out of the air by the leaves and branches of tree canopies, so the amount of acid deposited on the soil under trees can be several times greater than on adjacent open ground. Sulphur deposition levels near the edges of woodlands in Sweden have been shown to be about twice those in the general forest area. This is clearly liable to aggravate forest damage and the through-put of acidity to the soil. Acid pollution may also affect the micro-organisms (bacteria, fungi and algae) that trees depend on to break down organic matter into nutrients.

The susceptibility of forests to acid damage may depend on several different factors, including the species of tree, the neutralizing capacity and depth of soil, local climate, prevailing wind direction, and the deposition and altitude of forests (trees at higher altitudes or in enclosed valleys may receive more rain than those in lowlands, and may sometimes be enveloped in acid mist). Whatever the case, the critical agents of forest death probably vary from region to region (see Table 2.1).

Lakes, rivers and fish: declining signs of life

The effect of acid deposition on lakes is gradual, quiet and insidious. There are rarely any rotting corpses of fish or other visual evidence. "There is no muss, there is no fuss, there is no smell", observes Dr Harold Harvey of the University of Toronto. "The fish quietly go extinct...They simply fail to reproduce and become less and less abundant, and older and older, until they die out."[22] A survey of one Canadian lake – Lumsden Lake in the La Cloche mountains near Killarney, Ontario – revealed a clear timetable of change. In the 1950s the lake had eight species of fish. In 1960, two of the species were reported for the last time. In the period 1960–65 the sport fishery failed. In 1967, two more species were reported for the last time, and three more in 1969. By 1971, the one remaining species was very rare. By 1978, all the species were extinct.[23]

Changes in the biology of lakes provided one of the first clues to the problem of acid pollution. Links between the acidity of lakes and fish production were being investigated in Sweden and Norway before the second world war, but it was only in the 1950s and 1960s that the death of fish was linked with acidity in lakes.[24] By studying the shells of dead algae in lake sediments, Swedish researchers later found that the pH of lakes in Sweden had fallen from about 7.0 at the end of the last Ice Age 15,000 years ago to about 6.0 in 1949–50, when a more rapid decline began. Many lakes have since dipped below pH 5.0. A survey of fifteen lakes in western Sweden in the 1930s and 1940s found pH levels of 8–6.5; by 1971, the pH had fallen to 4.5.[25] More than a fifth of Sweden's 85,000 medium to large lakes are now acidified; about 4,000 are seriously acidified and have suffered major biological damage, and in about 9,000 – mainly in southern and central Sweden – fish stocks have been affected.[26]

Reports of declines in populations of fish, aquatic plant life and micro-organisms have also come from Canada, Norway and Scotland, and surface water acidification has been reported from Belgium, the Netherlands, Denmark, West Germany, Czechoslovakia, East Germany and the United States. In 1980, the Ontario Ministry of the Environment reported that 140 acidified lakes in the province had no fish at all, and a further 48,000 lakes would not be able to tolerate extended acid inputs.[27] Lake Donald, once one of Ontario's best bass and trout lakes, had lost all its fish by 1950. In 1973 it recorded a pH of 3.8.[28] In Norway's four southernmost counties, fish stocks have been halved since 1940. Lakes covering an area of more than 13,000 sq km (5,000 sq miles) contain no fish, and fish stocks have been reduced in a further 20,000 sq km (7,700 sq miles).[29] In New York's Adirondack mountains, the proportion of lakes above 600 m (2,000 ft) with pH values below 5.0 grew from 4% to 51% between the early 1930s and the early 1970s; 90% of the affected lakes had lost all their fish.[30]

As with forests, the exact routes to surface water acidification are not yet fully understood. The main problem is the lack of long-term records. In most cases, early measurements (where they exist) are questionable, and difficult to compare with more recent measurements.[31] The weakest link in the chain of scientific understanding is that between the chemical make-up of precipitation and the composition and acidity of lakes and streams. The problem here is that the composition of runoff and percolating water is the result of complex interactions between precipitation, melt-water, soil and vegetation, involving processes as different as weathering, cation exchange, buffering and the accumulation and release of pollutants.[32]

In brief, surface water can be acidified by direct deposition, by an increase in concentrations of mobile anions in runoff or percolating water, or through the acidification of adjacent soils. The susceptibility of lakes to acidification depends on the ability of adjacent soul to neutralize the acid, the extent and volume of surface runoff, the time the water is in contact with buffering substances in the soil/bedrock, the size of the catchment area, the distance from the river source, and the humus content of the water.[33]

There are three stages in the acidification of surface water. In the first stage, bicarbonate ions neutralize acids by reacting with hydrogen to produce carbon dioxide and water. Lakes have varying concentrations of negatively charged bicarbonate ions, the levels depending largely on the surrounding bedrock and soil. Where the soils have a high neutralizing capacity, few hydrogen ions will reach the lake, which will have high and stable levels of buffering bicarbonate ions. But lakes and watercourses in poorly buffered areas must use – and may exhaust – their bicarbonate ions. The natural formation of new bicarbonates (via carbonic acid from the air, weathering from the land, and decomposition of water plants) can be overwhelmed by continuous inputs of acid. As long as the bicarbonate content is maintained at a critical minimum level, the pH value of the water will remain stable, and plants, animals and micro-organisms will be unaffected. But a lake or watercourse subject to major acid inputs will be vulnerable.

In the second stage, the bicarbonate content drops below the critical level, and large influxes of hydrogen ions can no longer be neutralized. The pH value becomes unstable and begins to go down faster than before. Acid surges can drastically upset the delicate balance that remains. A sudden release of huge amounts of acidic water into the lake or watercourse – after the first thaw of spring in the northern hemisphere, or when heavy rains follow a period of drought – can be deadly, especially if it occurs when the organisms are at the most sensitive part of their life-cycle – for fish, when they are young (fry).

The third stage comes when the pH value stabilizes around 4.5, regardless of new influxes of hydrogen ions. Almost all the original life – including snails, crustaceans and many insects – is eliminated, fish disappear, and a small number of resilient animal and plant species predominate. An entirely new ecosystem emerges. The water becomes abnormally clear – visibility can increase from 4 to 5 m (12 to 15 ft) to anything from 15 to 20 m (50 to 65 ft) because the tiny plants that normally float in the surface waters, and the organic matter normally suspended in the lake, all die off. The rise in hydrogen ion content triggers a sequence of other, often more

---

Table 2.2: Biological effects of acid waters in Canada

pH	Effect
6.5	Continued exposure results in significant reduction in egg hatchability and growth in brook trout.
6.0	With high CO_2 concentrations, certain trout species can be adversely affected.
5.5–6.0	Rainbow trout not found. Small populations of relatively few fish species found. Molluscs rare.
5.5	Declines in salmon fisheries can be expected.
5.0–5.5	Restricted fish populations, but not lethal unless CO_2 is high. May be lethal to eggs and larvae, and to some mayflies. Diversity of bacterial species reduced.
5.0	Tolerable lower limit for most fish.
4.5–5.0	No viable fishery can be maintained. Lethal to eggs and fry of salmon species.
4.0–4.5	Fish population limited; few species survive. Flora restricted.

Source: Ministry of the Environment, Canada.

---

damaging, chemical changes. For example, the aluminium content of surface water may change. The aluminium content even of unaffected water can be quite high, especially if the water is rich in humus. One effect of soil acidification can be the release of aluminium ions, which function as a transport medium for hydrogen ions, into nearby groundwater and surface water.

The best researched effect of the acidification of inland waters is that on fish, which can die of aluminium poisoning even in lakes with moderate pH values. Aluminium in soluble inorganic form is thought to be especially toxic to fish. Almost as soon as fish hatch, the aluminium causes mucus clogging in the gills, which in turn reduces ion exchange across the membrane of the gills. Ion exchange is essential to the maintenance of the salt balance in the blood of fish. Reduced blood salts affect respiration, metabolism and cell volume, which can result in death. Acid in water can also kill fish eggs. Salmonid species, such as salmon and trout, are particularly sensitive to acidification. Fish can apparently adapt to a gradual lowering of pH, within limits, but rapid change, or acid surges following snow-melts, can lead to a permanent decline in fish populations.

The critical pH level for most aquatic species is 6.0. When the pH falls below this level, the number of species, and the population of algae, animal plankton, aquatic species, insect larvae, and sensitive fish (such as salmon, roach and minnow), declines. Below 5.5, the number of snails and microscopic plant species is reduced. Below 5.2, snails disappear. Below 5.0, many microscopic animal species disappear, and even the more tolerant species become rare.[34] Acidification affects the growth and productivity of many aquatic plant species, slows the bacterial decomposition of dead matter, and reduces the sources of food for birds and mammals that depend on freshwater ecosystems.

Plants and crops: the effects of ozone

Relatively little is known for certain about the links between air pollution and damage to crops and plants. Serious damage is widely suspected. A 1981 OECD study estimated that crop damage from SO_2 in eleven European countries cost about $500 million per

ACID DAMAGE 41

year.[35] In 1983, the annual cost of ozone damage to wheat, corn, soybeans and peanuts in the United States was estimated at roughly $3.1 billion;[36] in 1984, it was put at $1–2 billion annually.[37] Also in 1984, the Royal Commission on Environmental Pollution noted the general acceptance that background concentrations of sulphur and nitrogen oxides in the United Kingdom could "reduce the yields of some crops" (although, it went on, the magnitude of the effect was uncertain).[38]

Pollutants may damage plants and crops through short periods of high concentrations, or through prolonged exposure at lower concentrations; high peak concentrations are thought to be more critical than long-term exposure.[39] Acid deposition may also damage crops by affecting the balance of heavy metals in the soil. But sulphur and nitrogen can also act as fertilizers; indeed, small amounts of sulphur and nitrogen are essential to plants. Some plants can also develop a tolerance to SO_2.[40] As with trees, distinguishing damage caused by pollutants from damage caused by climate, pests, diseases or other factors is difficult. Most of the existing studies of the effects of acid deposition on plants have been carried out with SO_2, ozone or a combination of the two, and few have gone beyond laboratory experiments on the effects of long-term exposure. Experiments have shown that acid rain can damage the leaves of a variety of crops, but usually at pH levels well below those of typical rainfall.[41]

Studies to date show that the combined effect of two or three pollutants acting together synergistically is much more harmful than each acting alone. NO_x is thought to be less a cause of direct acute damage than other pollutants; although NO_x concentrations can reach high levels in rural areas, they are less easily absorbed by plants. NO_x also plays a role in the formation of ground level ozone, which may be a key element in pollution damage to crops and plants. Ozone can attack leaf cells and destroy chlorophyll, thereby lowering the rate of photosynthesis. The outer cells remain intact, giving the impression that the leaves are healthy. The damage eventually becomes visible as dark coloured spots or discoloured areas on the leaf surface. Tobacco plants show early visible signs of damage. Until the late 1950s this damage was called "weather fleck", but now it is recognized as ozone damage.[42]

There has also been conclusive evidence over the past twenty years of plant and crop damage from ozone during high summer concentrations in rurals areas of the United States. The most sensitive species are potatoes, dwarf beans, tobacco, tomatoes and radishes, all of which can experience visible leaf damage. Growth has also been affected in soybeans, winter/spring wheat and clover.[43] In 1980, the National Crop Loss Assessment Network investigated crop losses in the United States from ozone, SO_2 and NO_x. By studying the effect of ozone on the yield of several important crop species, it concluded that substantially greater yields of food crops would be available if ozone concentrations could be reduced from existing levels to "natural" levels (50 microgrammes). A panel of scientists appointed in 1982 by the Presidential Science Advisor supported the view that ozone caused crop damage.

Human health: killer smogs

In London, Tokyo, Mexico City, Sao Paulo and Beijing, millions of people have physically suffered the effects of air pollution.

Following the London smog of 1952, an estimated 4,000 people died from heart or lung ailments made worse by the smog (caused by smoke and SO_2), and many more fell ill. The very young, the elderly and those with heart and lung disorders were particularly vulnerable.[44] The litany of the most infamous killer smogs has now become all too familiar: London, 1873 and 1880 (2,500 deaths); Meuse Valley, Belgium, 1930 (63 deaths); Donora, Pennsylvania, 1948 (20 deaths, 14,000 ill); London, 1962 (340 deaths).[45]

The links between acid pollution and human illness are generally unclear. New warnings emerge regularly, linking pollution to everything from headaches to cancer, brain damage and senile dementia. Aluminium, for example, is associated with the development of Alzheimer's disease. So acid rain – by releasing aluminium into drinking water – could be implicated. A 1980 report argued that air pollution was responsible for as many as 50,000 premature deaths every year in the United States.[46]

In some cases, the evidence of a link between acid pollution and damage to health is strong, in others circumstantial. SO_2, sulphuric acid aerosol, and particulates are known to be linked with bronchitis, tracheitis, and respiratory problems, but the precise effect of different pollutants is still debated. As with forests and crops, the effect of one kind of pollutant may often reinforce the effects of others, making it difficult to identify the most damaging substance. Unfortunately for medical researchers, people breathe polluted air, not individual pollutants. It is also often difficult to disentangle the effects of pollution from such influences as social and economic status, diet, and the quality of health care.

Nevertheless, there is strong circumstantial evidence to link air pollution with damage to human health. The Katowice region of Poland offers a good example. The region constitutes 2% of Poland's land area, and is home to 10% of its population. It produces 31% of Poland's coke, 32% of its electricity, 52% of its steel, and 98% of its coal, and extracts and processes 100% of Poland's zinc and lead ores. Some of the cities in the region receive more than 1 kg/sq m (about 1 lb/5 sq ft) per year of industrial particle fallout. Many of the houses are built right up against the factories and smelters, and garden soils contain as much as 16 times the prescribed limits of cadmium and 44 times the lead limits.

The incidence of circulatory diseases in the region is 15% above the national average, and there are 30% more tumours and 47% more respiratory diseases. Of Poland's 102 schools for disabled and deformed children, 54 are in Katowice.[47] There is no proof that acid pollution is the cause of any or all of these health problems, but it is difficult to believe that there is no connection.

Acid pollution may pose a threat to health in three ways: (1) in the short-term, through breathing heavily polluted air (as in urban smogs); (2) in the long-term, through sustained breathing of air polluted at lower levels; (3) indirectly, through exposure to heavy metals or aluminium released into soils and water as a result of acidification, the accumulation of metals in the aquatic food chain, or heavy metals dissolved in acidic water supplied through lead or copper piping. Potentially harmful amounts of copper have been found in water in Sweden, Canada and the United States.[48]

SO_2 is a relatively non-toxic gas by comparison with carbon monoxide (CO) or NO_x, but high concentrations have been known to cause respiratory problems in humans. The World Health Organization recommends a maximum average atmospheric SO_2 concentration of 40–60 micrograms per cubic metre. Yet Stockholm, a relatively clean European capital in terms of air pollution, experienced concentrations as high as 180 micrograms in 1982–85. Milan meanwhile returned levels as high as 800 micrograms/cu.m..[49] Other pollutants that may be linked with damage to health include sulphates, nitrates and ozone (and other oxidants), polycyclic aromatic hydrocarbons, carbon monoxide, aluminium, arsenic, copper, and heavy metals such as lead, cadmium and mercury.

Corrosion: cultural heritage under attack

The corrosion of buildings and monuments is neither new nor surprising; soft building stones have always been eroded to some extent by the combined effects of wind and rain. The difference today is the degree of the problem. Theoretically, almost every building either in, or downwind of, a major urban or industrial centre may be at risk from the corrosive effects of acid deposition, and there is conclusive evidence that the rate of corrosion has increased dramatically in many urban areas. Buildings and structures which have stood largely undamaged for hundreds, even thousands, of years have recently begun to be affected. A Greek specialist on acid corrosion, Professor Theo Skoulikidis, has estimated that the deterioration of Athenian monuments in the past 20–25 years has been greater than in the previous 2,400 years, as a result of pollution.[50]

Most of the corrosion of city buildings and monuments is apparently the result of the dry deposition of SO_2 and sulphate particles, and is mainly due to high and localized urban concentrations of pollutants. Decay tends to happen in bursts rather than steadily or continuously. When sulphur pollutants fall on the surface of sandstone or limestone, for instance, they can react with the calcium carbonate in the stone to form gypsum (calcium sulphate), which sticks to the stone like icing on a cake. This causes flaking that can then be washed away by rainwater, exposing more stone to corrosion. Gypsum and soot particles can combine to form ugly black crusts on the sheltered surfaces of buildings. Acid attack can also lead to stone decay through the creation of salts, which can crystallize, expand and/or contract, bringing on fatigue or disintegration.[51] Salt weathering may in fact be the most important agent of decay.

Table 2.3: Air pollution damage to materials

Material	Effect	Principal air pollutants	Other factors
Metals	Corrosion, tarnishing	SO_2, acid gases	Moisture, air, particles, salt
Building stone	Surface erosion, soiling, black crust formation	Same as metals	Mechanical erosion, salt, particles, moisture, CO_2, temperature, vibration, micro-organisms
Ceramics and glass	Surface erosion, surface crust formation	Acid gases, esp. those containing fluoride	Moisture
Paints	Surface erosion, discolouration, soiling	SO_2 hydrogen sulphide	Moisture, ozone, sunlight, particles, mechanical errosion, micro-organisms
Paper	Embrittlement, discolouration	SO_2	Moisture, physical wear, acid used in manufacture
Photographic materials	Small blemishes	Same as paper	Moisture, particles
Textiles	Soiling and reduced tensile strength	SO_2, NO_x	Moisture, particles light, physical wear, washing
Leather	Weakening, powdered surface	SO_2	Physical wear, residual acids used in manufacture
Rubber	Cracking		Ozone, sunlight, physical wear

Source: Adapted from J.E. Yocom and N.S. Baer, 'Effects on Materials', in Environmental Protection Agency, *The Acidic Deposition Phenomenon and its Effects,* US EPA Critical Assessment Review Papers, Vol 2 (Washington, DC: EPA, 1983).

The rate of material corrosion is affected by two main factors:

o 1. the relative reactivity of the material to acidity. Stone and masonry that contain calcium carbonate or calcium sulphate are particularly susceptible. The pigments in paint can make paintwork susceptible, and humidity encourages metal corrosion.
o 2. meteorological conditions and the physical force of the delivery of pollutants. Humidity, air temperature, wind speed, and the intensity, duration and amount of rainfall are all important factors. Physical location is also important – the level of pollutants may be higher at street level than on the tenth floor.

The costs of acid pollution to the world's cultural heritage are causing increasing concern. The city of Krakow in Poland, one of the first to be included in the UNESCO list of sites of the world's cultural heritage, is downwind from Poland's industrial heartland. Its mediaeval buildings are under severe threat from the now frequent – and acidic – smogs that have made Krakow one of the most polluted cities in Europe. The city's buildings are corroding, and their walls and roofs are being weakened.[52]

Stained-glass windows are under threat. There are more than 100,000 stained-glass windows in Europe, some of them as much as 1,000 years old. There is evidence that much of this glass survived in relatively good condition until the turn of the century. Much survived even the second world war, when many stained-glass windows were taken down and stored. Within the last thirty years though, the damage which has occurred gives reason to fear that, unless effective measures are taken, the staining in many windows could fade within a matter of decades.

Up to 2.5 cm (1 inch) of the Portland stone on London's St Paul's Cathedral – which survived the wartime blitz – has been eaten away. Visitors making the climb to the dome and stepping outside onto the observation area are now greeted by the sight of lead pointing standing proud of the surrounding stone. Westminster Abbey in London, Cologne Cathedral in West Germany, the Coliseum and Trajan's Column in Rome, buildings in Bologna, Venice and Florence, and the Acropolis in Athens have all been damaged to varying degrees. In Venice, creamy white Istrian limestone is a common material in many buildings – it has withstood the rigours of pollution far less than the granite used in other Venetian buildings.[53] Until its 1984–85 restoration, the Statue of Liberty was visibly suffering the effects of wind, sea spray and air pollution. In Washington, DC, literally hundreds of monuments may be threatened.

Researchers at the US National Acid Precipitation Assessment Programme have found that chemical degradation removes 10–17 micrometres of stone per year, more than mechanical erosion.[54] In India, there is concern for the Taj Mahal. Emissions from an oil refinery built during the 1970s upwind from the monument may be threatening its marble and sandstone surfaces.[55] Pollution spreading indoors is suspected of damaging paintings, and has so concerned several major libraries and museums in the United States that they have fitted scrubbers to their ventilation systems.[56] Similar problems have been reported from several European libraries and archives.[57]

Stone is not the only material prone to damage; carbon steel, galvanized steel, copper, nickel, zinc, lead and cast-iron can all be corroded to varying degrees.[58] In the Katowice region of Poland, acid pollution has been blamed for corroding railway lines to such an extent that, in places, trains in 1981 were only allowed to travel at 40 kph (25 mph).[59] Even aluminium (in window frames, for example) can be attacked by acid. In precipitation with a pH less than 5.0, zinc and its surface coating of zinc carbonate become highly corrodable; zinc will corrode six times faster in polluted air than in clean air.[60] Readings taken in central Stockholm revealed that the rate of corrosion of zinc increased by 150% between 1938 and 1958.

The corrosion of materials may lead to even more dramatic effects, such as metal failure. According to the Swedish Corrosion Institute, concrete can be corroded in soil or water with pH values below 6.0. This has led to concern for the durability of concrete bridges, dams and other structures. Pollution could corrode metal reinforcement rods in concrete. For example, sulphur corrosion was implicated in the 1967 collapse of a steel highway bridge between West Virginia and Ohio in the United States, killing 46 people.[61] Theoretically, acid pollution could interfere with the airworthiness of an aeroplane, the structural strength of a building, or a vital electrical contact. A thin film of oxides could be formed on the electrical contact points in a computer, for example, so that a film no thicker than 0.0001 mm could in theory break down the operations of an entire industrial plant.

Submerged water and sewage pipes, telecommunications networks, electricity supply networks, galvanized road culverts and pole butts, anchor stays and wires, sluice gates, and piping in power stations could all be affected. Water pipes can be damaged from within and without. When copper pipes are attacked, the copper is dissolved in water and can cause discolouration of sanitary items and textiles, and even turn hair green. Polluted air can corrode paper, leather, textiles, plaster and household electrical contacts.

The cost to countries affected by atmospheric corrosion from sulphur compounds is estimated to be anywhere from $2 to $10 per capita per year, or between 0.10% and 0.23% of gross national product. With a population of 650 million, the costs to Europe could be between $1.3 billion and $6.5 billion per year.[62] In Sweden, the cost in corrosion to materials of all kinds has been estimated at $2.5 billion.[63] In the Netherlands, the cost in damage to monuments, libraries and archives was estimated in 1980 at $10–15 million a year.[64] In the United States, the Environmental Protection Agency estimated as long ago as 1974 that SO_2 emissions caused damage worth $2 billion to buildings. A study of damage to galvanized steel and painted steel in eleven OECD member countries in 1974 concluded that a 37% reduction in sulphur emissions would have saved nearly $1 billion at 1979 prices.[65]

NOTES

1. Schütt, Peter and Ellis Cowling, "Waldsterben, a general decline of forests in Europe: symptoms, development and possible causes", in *Plant Disease* 69:7, July 1985, pp. 548–58.
2. See note 1.
3. Pearce, Fred, "The strange death of Europe's trees", in *New Scientist*, December 1986, pp. 41–45.
4. Hinrichsen, Don, "Acid rain and forest decline", in Edward Goldsmith and Nicholas Hilyard (eds), *The Earth Report: The Essential Guide to Global Ecological Issues* (Los Angeles: Price Stern Sloan Inc., 1988).
5. Schütt and Cowling, see note 1.

6. Environmental Resources Limited, *Acid Rain: A review of the phenomenon in the EEC and Europe* (London: Graham and Trotman, 1983).

7. Federal Ministry of the Interior (West Germany), *Report of the Causes and Prevention of Damage to Forests, Waters and Buildings by Air Pollution in the Federal Republic of Germany* (Bonn: Ministry of the Interior, 1984).

8. Schütt and Cowling, see note 1.

9. Pearce, Fred, "The strange death of Europe's trees", in *New Scientist*, 4 December 1986, pp. 41–5.

10. Hinrichsen, Don, "Multiple pollutants and forest decline", in *Ambio* 15:5, 1986, pp. 258–65.

11. Ulrich, Bernhard and others in Rocco Fazzolare and Craig B. Smith (eds), *Beyond the Energy Crisis* (New York: Pergamon Press, 1981); and Bernhard Ulrich "An ecosystem oriented hypothesis on the effect of air pollution in forest ecosystems", in *Ecological Effects of Acid Deposition* (Solna, Sweden: National Swedish Environment Protection Board), Report PM 1636, 1983.

12. Schütt and Cowling, see note 1.

13. Ashmore, Mike, Nigel Bell and Jack Rutter, "The role of ozone in forest damage in West Germany", in *Ambio* 14:2, 1985, pp. 81–7.

14. Becker, K.H., J. Löbel, and U. Schurath, "Bildung, Transport und Kontrolle von Photo-oxidanten", in *Luftqualitätskriterien für photochemische Oxidanten* (Berlin: Erich Schmidt Verlag, 1983).

15. Ashmore and others, see note 13.

16. Duchelle, S.F., J.M. Skelly and B.I. Chevonne, "Oxidant effects on forest tree seedling growth in the Appalachian mountains", in *Water, Air and Soil Pollution* 18, 1982, pp. 363–73; and Mike Ashmore, "Effects of ozone on vegetation in the United Kingdom", in Peringe Grennefelt (ed.), *The Evaluation and Assessment of the Effects of Photochemical Oxidants on Human Health, Agricultural Crops, Forestry, Materials and Visibility* (Göteborg: Swedish Environmental Research Institute, 1984), pp. 92–104.

17. Hinrichsen, see note 10.

18. Schütt and Cowling, see note 1.

19. Nihlgard, Bengt, "The ammonium hypothesis – an additional explanation to the forest dieback in Europe", in *Ambio* 14:1, 1985, pp. 2–8.

20. See note 19.

21. See for example Andrew Friedland and others in *Journal of Water, Air and Soil Pollution* 26, 1984, p. 161.

22. Environment Canada, *Downwind: The Acid Rain Story* (Ottawa: Ministry of Supply and Services, Canada, 1982).

23. Harvey, Harold, "The acid deposition problem and emerging research

needs in the toxicology of fishes", in *Proceedings of the Fifth Annual Aquatic Toxicology Workshop* (Hamilton, Ontario, November 1978).

24. Cowling, Ellis B., "Acid precipitation in historical perspective", in *Environmental Science and Technology* 16:2, January 1982, pp. 110A–122A.

25. Environmental Resources Limited, *Acid Rain: A review of the phenomenon in the EEC & Europe* (London: Graham and Trotman, 1983).

26. *Acidification Today and Tomorrow* (Stockholm: Ministry of Agriculture, 1982).

27. Ministry of the Environment, Canada, *The Case Against the Rain*, Report on Acid Precipitation and Ontario Programs for Remedial Action, Ontario, 1980.

28. Environment Canada, see note 22.

29. *Acidification Today and Tomorrow*, see note 26.

30. *Acidification Today and Tomorrow*, see note 26.

31. Mason, Sir John and Hans Martin Seip, "The current state of knowledge on acidification of surface waters and guidelines for further research", in *Ambio* 14:1, 1985, pp. 45–51.

32. See note 31.

33. *Acidification Today and Tomorrow*, see note 26.

34. *Acidification Today and Tomorrow*, see note 26.

35. OECD, *The Costs and Benefits of Sulphur Oxide Control* (Paris: OECD, 1981).

36. Environmental Resources Limited, see note 25.

37. Skarby, Lena and Gun Selldén, "The effects of ozone on crops and forests", in *Ambio* 13:2, 1984, pp. 68–72.

38. Royal Commission in Environmental Pollution, *Annual Report 1984* (London: HMSO, 1985).

39. Environmental Resources Limited, see note 25.

40. Bell. J.N.B. and C.H. Mudd, "Sulphur dioxide resistance in plants: a case study of Lolium perenne", in T.A. Mansfield (ed.), *Effects of Air Pollutants on Plants* (London: Elsevier, 1976).

41. Gould, Roy, *Going Sour: Science and Politics of Acid Rain* (Boston: Birkhäuser, 1985), p. 74.

42. Strauss, W. and S.J. Mainwaring, *Air Pollution* (London: Edward Arnold, 1984).

43. Environmental Resources Limited, see note 25.

44. Ashby, Eric and Mary Anderson, *The Politics of Clean Air* (Oxford: Clarendon Press, 1981).

45. See note 44; Chris C. Park, *Acid Rain: Rhetoric and Reality* (London: Methuen, 1987).

46. Wilson, R., S.D. Colome, J.D. Spengler and D.G. Wilson, *Health Effects*

of Fossil Fuel Burning (Cambridge, MA: Ballinger, 1980).
47. Timberlake, Lloyd, "Poland – the most polluted country in the world?" in *New Scientist*, 22 October 1981, p. 246.
48. Environmental Resources Limited, see note 25.
49. WRI/IIED, *World Resources 1988–89* (New York: Basic Books Inc., 1988).
50. Skoulikidis, Theo N., "Effects of primary and secondary air pollutants and acid depositions on (ancient and modern) buildings and monuments." Paper presented to symposium on Acid Deposition: A Challenge for Europe, Commission of the European Communities, Karlsruhe, September 1983.
51. Smith, Bernard, Brian Whalley and Vasco Fassina, "Elusive solution to monumental decay", in *New Scientist*, 2 June 1988, pp. 49–53.
52. Timberlake, see note 47.
53. Smith, Whalley, Fassina, see note 51.
54. Joyce, Christopher, "US assesses the toll of decay on its national heritage", in *New Scientist*, 2 June 1988, p. 52.
55. D'Monte, Darryl, "Taj Mahal threatened, while experts debate", in *Ambio* 12:2, 1983, pp. 130–31.
56. Yocom, J.E. and N.S. Baer, "Effects on materials", in *The Acidic Deposition Phenomenon and its Effects* (Washington, DC: EPA Critical Assessment Review Papers, Vol 2, 1983).
57. Muntingh, I., Information Note on Acid Rain, European Parliament, 1983, quoted in Nigel Dudley, Mark Barrett and David Baldock, *The Acid Rain Controversy* (London: Earth Resources Research, 1985).
58. Baboian, Robert, (ed.), *Materials Degradation Caused by Acid Rain* (Washington DC: American Chemical Society, 1986).
59. Timberlake, see note 47.
60. UN Economic Commission for Europe, *Report on the Effects of Sulphur Compounds on Materials, Including Historic and Cultural Monuments* (Geneva: UNECE, 1982).
61. Gerhard, J. and E.H. Haynie, *Air Pollution Effects on Catastrophic Failure of Metals*, EPA–650/3–74–009, Research Triangle Park, North Carolina, 1974.
62. Figures from UN Economic Commission for Europe.
63. Research at the Swedish Corrosion Institute, reported in *Land* (Sweden), 20 January 1984.
64. Figures from Dutch Ministry of Health and Environmental Protection 1980.
65. OEDC 1981, see note 35.

3. Reducing and Controlling Acid Pollution

Speaking at the 1982 Stockholm Conference on Acidification of the Environment, James MacNeill, then environment director of OECD, observed that emission control was no longer primarily a technological issue, because the technology existed and was known to work. "Neither is the issue the balance between the costs and benefits of control", he said. "The principal issue and the main source of controversy is who should bear the costs, how should the costs be borne, and when." Whether the emissions from power stations are controlled or not, pollution imposes costs. If emissions are controlled, the costs will have to be borne by power companies, industry and the taxpayer. If emissions are not controlled, then the costs will be borne by everyone who suffers the consequences of dead forests and lakes, acidified soils, and polluted cities.

There are four main routes to cutting pollutive emissions: (1) using low-pollutant fuels; (2) preventing the formation of pollutants during combustion; (3) screening pollutants from exhaust and flue gases; (4) energy conservation. Within each of these options, there are many sub-options, several of which have been available for many years. For the policy-maker, this is both a blessing and a curse: a blessing because of the range of options available, but a curse because of the difficulties of achieving consensus both on the best technology in a given situation and on who should pay. This is complicated by the fact that there is often little agreement on whether a particular technological option is readily and immediately practicable, has short-term potential, or is simply a theoretical possibility.[1]

There are obvious technical, economic and environmental advantages to equipping a power station or smelter with emission controls from the outset, but retrofitting is another matter. Many governments and energy authorities baulk at the costs involved in retrofitting existing power plants, and plead the case for more certainty about the economic benefits. The view of many scientists and acid pollution lobbyists is that any decrease in deposition will benefit the environment and people's health, so any control measures are better than none. Delegates to the 1982 Stockholm conference concluded that "the mere fact that better technology may come along in the future would not justify us in waiting and delaying the utilization of already existing technology for the reduction of emissions."

Using low-sulphur oil and coal

Using low-sulphur fuels may seem a simple and obvious solution, but supplies (especially of oil) are limited. Low-sulphur crudes are almost always light, and are more expensive because they yield more valuable refined products. They accounted for only a fifth of total world oil reserves and for about 30% of total oil production in 1980. The regions with the biggest reserves of oil – the Middle East (55% of world reserves) and Latin America (nearly 11%) – produce crude oil with a high sulphur content (1.4–1.6%). Hence future oil supplies will continue to depend heavily on high-sulphur oil.

Reserves of low-sulphur coal are more plentiful. Defined as coal containing 1% sulphur or less, low-sulphur coal makes up 100% of Australian and western US reserves, and 90% of South African reserves. But low-sulphur coal is unequally distributed. For example, a shift to low-sulphur coal is difficult in the United States because the biggest market for coal is in the mid-west. This region uses mainly high-sulphur mid-western coal because the biggest low-sulphur reserves are further away in the west. Boilers in many plants were designed to use high-sulphur coal and would need expensive refitting to use low-sulphur coal efficiently.[2] The US coal industry is also worried that a switch to low-sulphur coal would threaten jobs in the high-sulphur mines of the east. Congressmen from West Virginia – the main source of high-sulphur coal – have done all they can to block acid rain legislation in Congress, fearing not only the loss of their own jobs but of jobs in one of the poorest regions of the country.

Control before combustion

The amount of sulphur and nitrogen given off by fossil fuels can be reduced by exposing the fuels to physical or chemical processes that remove some of the sulphur or nitrogen before the fuels are burned. Coal is normally cleaned as a matter of course to remove incombustible particles of sand, clay and other materials. The cleaning usually takes place at the mine, and produces coal with a higher energy value, a less variable sulphur content and reduced ash content. It can cost less to ship, handle and store, has better boiler reliability and – because of the reduced slagging (formation of cinders) – reduces the costs of maintaining boilers. On the other hand, the cleaning process also produces high-sulphur waste which has to be disposed of safely, and about 10% of the energy content of coal is lost in the process.[3]

The sulphur in coal is partly pyritic (fixed to mineral grains in the form of iron sulphide) and partly organic (a chemically bonded part of the coal itself), usually in equal proportions. Physically washing out the pyrites is a relatively simple matter of crushing the coal and putting it through a large water tank; the coal floats while the impurities sink to the bottom. This can remove anything from 20 to 35% of the sulphur in coal,[4] with a subsequent reduction in SO_2 emissions of 8 to 33%.[5] Removing organic sulphur demands more complex and expensive chemical processes, based on such methods as the use of microwave energy or electron beams (a method still in its infancy). Chemical treatment can remove both pyritic and organic sulphur, but most methods are still at the pilot study stage, and none are likely to be commercially viable until the early 1990s.[6] Although laboratory tests show possible sulphur reduction rates as high as 90%, high costs, high energy losses and potential engineering problems make chemical processes less commercially attractive.[7]

Physical coal cleaning is used commercially in several countries, including West Germany and the United States. In the United States, 40% of the hard coal and lignite coal produced in 1976 in eleven eastern and mid-western states was cleaned. The result was an estimated reduction in SO_2 emissions of 2.4 million tonnes. If all coal produced in these states was treated with currently available technology, SO_2 emissions could be reduced by more than 5 million tonnes,[8] a more than 20% reduction in total US emissions. The OECD has estimated that if all the hard coals (coals other than lignite) used in Western Europe were washed, SO_2 emissions could be reduced by about a million tonnes a year (5% of the annual total) at an annual cost of $350 million.

One apparently cheap and simple physical coal cleaning technique still in its experimental stages uses a dry electrostatic process to remove pyritic sulphur and ash from crushed coal.[9] The coal is fed into a rotating drum and electrostatically charged. The coal particles are attracted to the drum, and the sulphur and ash are thrown free. Trials suggest that the system – developed by the US firm Advanced Energy Dynamics – could remove 30–68% of the sulphur and 50–60% of the ash. Trials funded by the US Environmental Protection Agency achieved a 52% sulphur removal at less than half the cost (per tonne of product coal) of conventional washing methods.

One drawback with coal cleaning is that it produces a large amount of solid waste. On the other hand, it demands little power plant modification, reduces transport costs, may improve the combustion process, and can be used effectively in conjunction with other combustion or post-combustion control methods.[10] Its reliability and relative low cost also make it a potentially workable policy option for Third World countries.

Oil desulphurization

During refining, most of the sulphur in oil ends up in heavy oils with a sulphur content of 3–5.5% (compared to 0.2–0.7% in light oils). The sulphur content of these heavy oils can then be reduced to as little as 0.5% by techniques already widely used in refineries.

Indirect oil desulphurization (or hydro-desulphurization) is a simple and commercially well-established technique, particularly in Japan. During refining, the light oils (or distillates) produced by the distillation of crude oil are distilled again, this time under vacuum. The product of this second distillate is "hydro-treated" so that the sulphur is made to react with hydrogen. This hydro-treated distillate is then blended with the heavy oil to yield a low-sulphur fuel oil product. This can reduce the original sulphur content of the oil by 30–42%.[11] The different factors involved make it difficult to estimate the overall cost of oil desulphurization, but estimated costs for oil with a sulphur content of 1 to 3% range from $25 to $50 per tonne, depending on the process chosen.

According to OECD calculations, indirect desulphurization capacity in Western Europe could be increased from its present level to reduce SO_2 emissions by about 3 million tonnes (or 15%). But the declining demand for fuel oils, and the world oil surplus (including naturally low-sulphur oils) has generally discouraged oil companies from investing in desulphurizing equipment. In addition, few European countries other than Sweden have stringent regulations on sulphur content in heavy fuel oil. Direct desulphurization, which is potentially far more effective, has not yet been commercialized. In this method, the residue from the initial distillation is reacted with hydrogen and then reblended with the distillate to produce a lower sulphur oil. Alternatively, both the residue and the distillate are separately hydro-treated before reblending. This can remove up to 90% of the sulphur.[12]

Control during combustion

The burning of fuels can be controlled to reduce the amounts of sulphur and nitrogen compounds released. Methods developed so far have been aimed at reducing both SO_2 and NO_x emissions. Most have just been introduced, or are about to be introduced commercially. Because of the time needed to plan, design and build new furnaces, most of these systems will not provide anti-pollution dividends for some time to come.

Lime injection in multistage burners (LIMB)
This technique, which has been under development since the 1960s, controls SO_2 and NO_x emissions and is basically a combination of the low-NO_x burning method (see below) and sulphur removal methods. Where powdered coal is used, an absorbant (usually powdered limestone) is injected into the firebox and the combustion temperature lowered by using special burners. The limestone reacts with the sulphur to convert much of it into calcium sulphate dihydrate (gypsum).

LIMB may be able to cut SO_2 emissions by 50–70% and NO_x

emissions by half, by the time it is ready for commercial use.[13] It can also be easily and cost-effectively retrofitted into existing plants. The capital investment of $30–40/kW of plant capacity is far lower than for flue gas desulphurization (FGD – see below), making LIMB even more attractive for retrofitting in plants and installations where FGD cannot be installed because of a lack of space. The costs of retrofitting have traditionally been used to argue against immediate action to reduce emissions from existing plants. The availability of LIMB undermines this argument to some extent.

Simple, low-cost techniques similar to LIMB have been developed in several countries (including Austria, East Germany and West Germany) to remove sulphur from brown coal. Calcium oxide, calcium carbonate or calcium hydroxide is added to the brown coal before combustion. These so-called dry additive processes can remove 40–60% of the sulphur.

Fluidized bed combustion (FBC)
In this system, the fuel is burned in a perforated bed containing mineral material (generally limestone or dolomite) and residual ash from previously burned coal. Air is blown into the combustion chamber, causing the particles to float freely and behave as a liquid; hence the term "fluidized bed." Combustion takes place without visible flames at a temperature of about 850 to 900°C (1,560 to 1,650°F), much less than the 1,650°C (3,000°F) needed in conventional coal-fired systems. The lower temperature reduces the formation of NO_x from nitrogen in the air, but has less effect on the oxidation of nitrogen in the fuel. Most of the SO_2 reacts with the bed material to produce gypsum. SO_2 removal rates of up to 90% are possible.[14]

All the available information indicates that the fluidized bed technique is economically competitive with conventional coal-fired systems. There are several distinct advantages to FBC: it tackles pollutant emissions at source in the furnace; high-grade and low-grade coal can be used, making fluidized bed plants often more economical than stoker-fired plants; fuels heat up rapidly and evenly, so combustion efficiency is high (generally about 95%); an FBC boiler takes up less space than boilers with other firing systems; construction is simple and rugged; personnel requirements are low, and overall investment costs are low. A 1986 UN survey found that the FBC process could remove sulphur at a cost of $234 per tonne.[15] For small plants, FBC is often the only economically feasible desulphurization method.

In addition to the conventional atmospheric fluidized bed boiler (AFBC), the pressurized fluidized bed (PFBC) system – which passes air onto the combustion bed through the compressor of a gas turbine – has been under recent investigation. In theory, pressurization should improve the efficiency of SO_2 and NO_x removal. An experimental PFBC system (the largest in the world) was built in the United Kingdom in 1985 with funding from that country, the United States and West Germany, but was abandoned in early 1988 when it was found that it would not be economical for anything other than small power stations (see chapter 5).

NO_x reduction during combustion
Because NO_x is formed by the effect of combustion on nitrogen in the air and in fuel, lowering the combustion temperature and reducing the time air stays in the combustion chamber can reduce its formation. The simplest option is to modify the burner so that the fuel and air mix more slowly, reducing the intensity and temperature of combustion. The air used in combustion is split into several streams and introduced into the flame in stages. Low-NO_x burners like these can cut NO_x emissions by 30–50%.[16]

The attractions of low-NO_x burners (first used in 1962) are that NO_x reduction becomes part of the plant design and operation, and equipment costs are relatively low. A low-NO_x burner may cost 50% more than a regular burner, but this amounts to only about 2% of the total cost of the whole boiler. But if NO_x emissions are to be reduced significantly, burners and other similar staged combustion processes must also be retrofitted into existing plants.

Integrated coal gasification combined cycle (IGCC)
One process still in its developmental stage, but which has shown great promise for SO_2 and NO_x reduction, combines two existing

technologies: gasification and combined cycle. Coal is crushed and mixed with water to form a slurry. This is fed into a gasifier along with a stream of almost pure oxygen. Under pressure and at high temperatures, the coal is converted into a synthetic gas made up mainly of carbon monoxide and hydrogen. The gas is cooled, producing steam and an inert slag. Sulphur is then removed from the gas, and the gas is heated to drive a gas turbine. Exhaust from the gas turbine is combined with steam from the coolers to drive a steam turbine. Both turbines generate electricity; hence the term "combined cycle."

A model $263 million plant in the Mojave Desert, 160 km (100 miles) east of Los Angeles, has removed up to 99% of the sulphur from coal. The inert slag produced by the gasifier can be sold for road building, insulation and abrasives, and the almost pure extracted sulphur for use in making sulphuric acid and fertilizers. Another key advantage of the process is that it can be used with high-sulphur coal. According to the Electrical Power Research Institute, funded by American power companies to research new technologies, the process could generate electricity at a cost of 4–5 cents/kW hour, making it very competitive with existing systems.[17]

Post-combustion control

Flue gas desulphurization (FGD) – in which sulphur is removed from the gases given off by coal-burning – has been used commercially for several years, and is the most immediate and widely used method for reducing SO_2 emissions. More than 1,000 plants already use it; most of these are in Japan and the United States, but FGD is also in use (or planned) in Austria, Britain, Bulgaria, Czechoslovakia, Finland, the Netherlands, Norway, Poland, Sweden, the Soviet Union, West Germany, and Yugoslavia.[18] The process removes much of the SO_2 formed during combustion by spraying or "scrubbing" the flue gases (exhaust gases) in the chimney with a chemical absorbent, usually lime or limestone. There are two types of FGD: wet and dry.

Wet FGD is the more widely used of the two options, and was first introduced in Japan and the United States in the mid-1960s. Two types of wet scrubbers are currently in operation: those using a recovery process, where the absorbent is regenerated and recirculated to the system, and those using non-recovery. Non-recovery – by far the more widely used – uses lime or limestone, sodium alkali, or dilute sulphuric acid as an absorbent. The gases are sprayed with a slurry of water and lime, limestone or caustic or soda ash. The SO_2 reacts with this slurry, and comes off as a wet sludge, a calcium sulphite and calcium sulphate mixture with the consistency of toothpaste. Other wet scrubbing processes use ammonia (the Walther process), magnesium oxide (the Mag-Ox process), sodium citrate, sodium carbonate, or sodium sulphite (the Wellman-Lord process).

The advantages of the wet method are that it can remove 90–95% of the SO_2 formed during combustion, and that it is tried and tested, making it more versatile and readily available than most other control options. The costs of wet FGD vary with the different processes and with local needs and conditions, but investment costs generally come to about 15–20% of the total cost of a power plant. Energy costs might increase by about 10%. The removal of one tonne of sulphur can cost $400–1,000.

The biggest disadvantage with wet FGD systems is the sludge they produce, which is difficult to dehydrate, store and handle. In a typical 1,000 MW plant, burning coal with 3.5% sulphur, wet FGD produces about 225,000 tonnes of sludge annually.[19] A 1982 report concluded that the United States would produce more sludge from FGD scrubbers than from the treatment of municipal sewage.[20] The sludge can be recovered, but the recovery processes are expensive and energy-intensive, and so have been little used except where other factors – such as limited space for sludge disposal – have had to be taken into account. Recovery processes can extract sulphuric acid or pure sulphur from the sludge waste, and this can in turn be sold commercially. Using air oxidation, the calcium sulphate can also be converted into gypsum. Japan has little natural gypsum, so has developed ways of purifying and marketing the converted gypsum. Wet FGD also raises the problem of how to prevent toxic metals, like mercury, leaking from residual fly ash and sludge and contaminating groundwater. But sludge can be chemically treated to reduce the water content and improve its compressive strength.

Dry FGD has evolved partly in response to the problems of sludge produced by the wet method. First successfully used in large-scale operation in 1980, dry FGD can use two different processes. In the Saarberg-Hölter process, lime slurry or soda ash is sprayed into the flue gases, absorbing the SO_2 and being dried at the same time; in the Walther process, ammonia is sprayed into the gases, producing pelletized ammonium sulphate as a dry end product. The pellets can then be used as fertilizers.

Dry scrubbers produce waste that is easier to handle and use. They also have fewer operating problems, need fewer operators, have lower capital, operating and maintenance costs, and use much less water than other systems. But lime is an expensive reagent, and dry scrubbers use more energy and remove less SO_2 than wet scrubbers (50–90%).[21] They are not yet widely used, mainly because they are most effective with low- or medium-sulphur coals.

The electron beam method

One FGD process still at the pilot stage is the electron-beam (E-beam) system. It promises simultaneous removal of SO_2 and NO_x, plus the production of a saleable by-product, by actually creating "acid rain" at source. Flue gas is sprayed with water to reduce its temperature to 60–90°C (140–195°F), and then further sprayed with ammonia. The cooled gas mixture then passes through an electron beam reactor which turns the oxides into acids. These react with the ammonia and water vapour to form ammonium compounds that can be used in fertilizers. Laboratory tests have shown that 80–92% of the SO_2 and 50–90% of the NO_x can be captured. Trials by the US Department of Energy's Advanced Environmental Control Technology Program began at two American power stations early in 1984.[22] Another E-beam system being tested at a Tennessee Valley Authority power plant produces calcium sulphate, nitrate and ash which can be reacted with lime to produce a solid substance suitable for landfill.

Flue gas treatment for NO_x reductions

Several attempts have been made to develop post-combustion techniques that remove NO_x from flue gases, and there are now at least fifty such processes.[23] Some methods are currently being used in Japan in oil-fired boilers. Most of the commercially applied methods use selective catalytic reduction (SCR), where ammonia is added to the furnace exhaust gases and the mixture subsequently passed over a fixed bed catalyst, such as copper oxide. This can remove 80–90% of the NO_x and convert it into elementary nitrogen. The problem is that SCR is more expensive than the low-NO_x burner, so it is doubtful how widely it will be used. NO_x reductions of 40–70% have been achieved with non-catalytic reduction, where ammonia is injected directly into the combustion zone. The OECD estimates capital costs of SCR at \$15–60/kW of plant capacity (depending on boiler size and whether heat recovery systems are included), and \$7–15/kW for non-catalytic systems.[24]

Cutting vehicle emissions

As the source of 33–50% of non-natural emissions of NO_x (the proportion varies by country), road traffic is a major target for emission control technology. The most readily available system (for petrol-driven vehicles, but not for diesel) is the catalytic converter, already widely used in the United States and Japan. The three-way converter reduces emissions of NO_x, CO and hydrocarbons (HC). Fitted to the vehicle exhaust, it contains either beads or a honeycomb-like structure coated with a combination of the precious metals platinum (85%) and rhodium (15%). About two grammes of precious metal is needed for each converter. The spent exhaust gases from the engine pass through the converter, which oxidizes CO and HC to CO_2 (carbon dioxide) and H_2O (water), and reduces NO_x to nitrogen. CO, NO_x and HC emissions can be reduced by up 90% in a motor vehicle in ordinary traffic, provided the converter is well maintained.

But the three-way converter also has three disadvantages. First, it is complex. In order to function effectively, the air/fuel mix in the combustion chamber must be carefully controlled. Second, it is sensitive to lead and so is useless in the many countries that still rely wholly or largely on leaded petrol. Third, it is fairly expensive. The annual average cost (purchase of the converter plus maintenance over ten years) works out from \$60 to \$80 upwards per car. Doubts have also arisen about its long-term benefits. US studies show that illegal switches back to leaded petrol (which used to be cheaper than unleaded petrol in the United States) and improper operation and maintenance can substantially reduce the effectiveness of converters. Hence their use needs to be compulsory, or linked to public education about their long-term environmental and health benefits.

The UK government has been particularly doubtful about catalytic converters. In March 1984 the Department of Transport argued that catalytic converters then available "would worsen fuel economy" and add about £2 billion per year to motoring costs, and that such expenditure was not justified for vehicle emissions in the United Kingdom.[25] UK motor manufacturers promised in 1979 to work towards reducing petrol consumption on new cars by 10% by 1985, a target that was passed and exceeded in 1983, mainly through the development of high compression "lean-burn" engines. They argued then that savings as high as 17% would have been achieved but for the terms of EC directives on emission reductions, and still maintain that lean-burn technology reduces NO_x emissions. They continue to argue that catalytic converters are a "cul-de-sac technology" that is prohibitively expensive.

European motor manufacturers have argued that European driving conditions – including urban stop-start motoring and high motorway speeds – mean that converters will not perform as well as they have in the United States, which has less congested roads and a blanket speed limit of 90 kph (55 mph, raised to 105 kph/65 mph on most interstate highways in 1987). This has been disputed by Johnson Matthey, the world's biggest manufacturer of converters, which quotes a test in which a vehicle fitted with a converter was driven for 80,000 km (50,000 miles) at an average 170 kph (105 mph) and still met US emission standards at the end of the test.[26] (The great irony in this is that Johnson Matthey is a UK company and its catalytic converters are routinely attached to cars sold in the United States.)

The 1984 House of Lords committee (see chapter 5) concluded that the three-way catalyst "efficiently reduces all three major pollutants. . .It is the only available technology which has a proven record of controlling emissions."[27] Nonetheless, in late

1986, Ford announced plans to spend £550 million to develop a new generation of lean-burn engines, emphasizing the preference among UK manufacturers for the lean-burn option. Certainly, lean-burn engines do reduce NO_x emissions, but not as effectively as catalytic converters, and not when cars are travelling at high speeds.

Energy conservation

Most of the debate over controlling acid pollution has centred on methods of reducing the amount of emission caused by fossil fuel combustion. Relatively little attention is paid to actually reducing the amount of fuel burned in the first place: energy conservation. The developed countries that account for 80% of the world's consumption of commercial energy still rely largely on methods developed in an age of cheap and plentiful energy, when efficient use of energy was less important. Hence many of the technologies used in power stations are grossly inefficient, a great deal of energy is lost during conversion and distribution, and end-consumers in the public and private sectors use energy inefficiently.

The United Kingdom provides an example of the inefficient use of energy. According to the influential *A Low Energy Strategy for the United Kingdom*, published in 1979, the United Kingdom could have cut its energy consumption in half in the early 1980s at no cost to its standard of living or level of economic activity.[28] Most UK power stations (which generate more than 80% of the UK's electricity) have poor thermal efficiency: as much a two-thirds of the heat generated by a power station can be lost because of the low efficiency of converting coal to electricity. Up to one-fifth of primary energy is lost through the cooling towers of power stations. More losses are sustained through inadequate insulation at the point of consumption – in factories, businesses, shops and private homes.

Transport provides similar problems. The number of road vehicles has been increasing steadily throughout the world. In the United Kingdom there has been a 400% increase since 1953, and three times as many kilometres are now travelled in cars than in all other forms of land transport combined. The proportion in the United States is even higher: American loyalty to the private car is made only too obvious by the decaying public transport system, and the widespread lack of pavements for pedestrians. Yet road vehicles are still far from fuel-efficient, partly because of body and engine design and partly because of the way they are driven. As little as 12% of the fuel put into a car is actually converted into useful motive power at the wheels. Nearly 62% is expelled by the exhaust or used up in cylinder cooling, and much of the rest is lost in air drag and tyre drag.

The most efficient use of petrol is made in cars travelling at a steady 90 kph (55 mph). The 55 mph limit imposed in the United States in response to the energy crises in the 1970s helped reduce national petrol consumption there by one-fifth between 1978 and 1984. Since then, though there has been a glut of oil; in 1988–89, petrol prices ranged from about 80c–$1 per gallon (about 57–72p per imperial gallon). Speed limits have also been raised to 65 mph (105 kph) on most interstate highways. Despite periodic clamp-downs by state police departments motivated by federal government threats of witholding highway grants unless speed limits are respected, those limits are assiduously ignored, especially in cities. The combined effect of cheap petrol and higher speeds has been to raise fuel consumption. The trend to smaller, more fuel-efficient cars which began during the energy crises has also been eased in the United States. The new wisdom seems to have been best summed up by a television commercial during 1988 for a popular luxury car. It was based on the single, simple sales pitch that the car was longer than its main competitor.

World energy consumption is predicted to grow by 225% in the next forty years. William Chandler of the Washington-based Worldwatch Institute observes that, if this prediction comes true, sulphur emissions will – without emission controls – increase by 265% over current levels. "Energy conservation could hold these releases to a 35% increase," he notes, "and make the use of emission controls more affordable and feasible."[29] Energy conservation, improved energy-use efficiency, speed limits, and the increased use of public transport could all help industrialized countries in particular to reduce the quantities of fossil fuels burned, and thereby lead to a reduction in the quantity of pollutive emissions. Because of its low costs and quantifiable economic advantages, conservation also has a particular immediacy in developing countries which are striving to reduce their oil and coal import bills.

Liming: treating the symptoms

Liming counters acidity by helping to restore the natural buffering capacity of lakes and watercourses. Lime, limestone and dolomite have been used for the liming of lakes, streams and rivers in Sweden, Norway and Canada since the mid-1970s. Sweden has the most experience and most complete documentation of liming. A test programme was started there in 1976, and large-scale liming has been in progress since 1982. Two methods have been used: adding lime (mostly in the form of finely crushed limestone) directly into the water, or liming the land around the lake and small brooks feeding the lake.

When lime is added directly to the lake, 50–90% of it is absorbed and pH values immediately fall. Liming surrounding land or catchment areas has less immediate effects (the lime flows into the lake water at an estimated rate of about 2% per year), but has ecological advantages. It avoids potentially harmful alkaline surges, neutralizes the acid deposition before it reaches the lake, and prevents the leaching of aluminium and other toxic metals from the soil at the same time as it restores the bicarbonate content of the soil water. But the relative costs of catchment-area liming are much higher because of the small proportion of lime that reaches lakes during the course of a year. It can also harm wildlife.

About 3,000 Swedish lakes have been limed to date, with the following results:

- The water has been rapidly recolonized by plankton and winged insects.
- Reproduction of fish has been restored in lakes where there were still enough fish left. (In severely acidified lakes with no fish, new stocks must be introduced at additional cost).
- Sources of nutrition for amphibians and fish-eating birds have been restored.
- Mercury content in fish has decreased, since the metal is once again fixed to the bottom sediments.

But liming has had many drawbacks. First, metals from surrounding land have continued to wash into lakes, carried by acid soil water.

Metals released from the lake sediments during acidification have remained; although temporarily fixed by the added lime, they are not rendered permanently harmless. If liming stops or goes below a critical level, the metals go into solution again. In other words, liming is habit-forming.

Second, the direct input of acid water and the short retention time of lake water makes it difficult to maintain the positive effects of liming for any length of time. The turn-over time of the water determines how often the liming should be repeated. In Sweden, liming generally lasts about three to five years, but Norway's test programme has had shorter turn-over times. Norwegian acidified lakes are mostly small and situated in the upper reaches of water systems with small catchment areas. Acid surges (especially during snow-melt) are difficult to control with liming. If acid surges have already killed fish fry and other organisms in the sensitive spawning season, raising the pH of the lakes is futile.

Third, many watercourses are difficult to lime; maintaining adequate pH levels in longer streams is particularly difficult. In mountain streams the water may run so fast that not even a soil naturally high in lime has time to neutralize the runoff. Attempts to lime running waters, streams and rivers have been discouraging. The equipment used to add the lime to the waters continuously is expensive and is neither very efficient nor very reliable. Lake liming costs about $30 per tonne of lime spread. By 1984, the Swedish liming programme had already cost $25 million.

Above all, though, the major doubt about liming is that it is an artificial, chemical attempt to maintain "natural conditions" in freshwater ecosystems, and that it is tackling the symptoms rather than the causes. Even worse, it is passing the costs on to the victims of acidification rather than the producers of the pollutive emissions.

Liming soils and groundwater

A Swedish test programme was launched on 1982 to study ways of countering soil and groundwater acidification. Dolomite was used in combination with ash and added phosphorous, potassium and boron as a liming agent. By 1985, $2 million had been spent on the programme. Forest-land liming has not been carried out long enough to show any hard results, but evaluations of forest land limed 20–25 years ago (with the aim of improving site quality in general) offer little cause for hope or optimism. The liming has damaged soil organisms and leached nitrate from the soils, and has actually impaired forest growth rather than encouraging it.

In the longer term, soil liming can raise the pH value and cation content of the soil, make aluminium less mobile, and help keep soils healthier until acid deposition is reduced to the point where natural neutralizing systems can take over. Liming could, at best, maintain adequate soil conditions and prevent an increase in stress subject to continued direct pollution damage. Once emissions decreased and direct damage stopped, the better soil conditions would promote tree growth.

Policy implications: the costs of pollution control

Prohibitive cost is the most common element in arguments used by governments and industries opposed to taking action to control emissions. They argue that emission controls will add to the costs of using coal and oil, that the economic advantages of coal over other fossil fuels will be reduced, that the costs will have to be passed on in higher fuel bills to the consumer, and that production levels will decrease and unemployment levels increase.

Estimates of cost vary widely. A 1982 OECD symposium on the costs of coal pollution abatement pointed out that the data then available on the price of SO_2 abatement had "an unacceptable range of variation."[30] Costs for wet FGD varied from \$72 to \$207/kW, a range which reflected differences in plant capacity, sulphur removal rates, the sulphur content of coal, and varying methods of accounting. Estimates made by the electricity industries in the United States and the United Kingdom are varied and often exaggerated. The US electrical industry estimates that a 30% SO_2 reduction from twenty-four generating stations would eat up 23–58% of total cash flow, double the capital costs, treble the operating costs, and raise electricity prices by 5.7% over a decade. When President Bush announced his acid pollution control plans in June 1989, it was estimated that they would cost \$16–19 billion per year (for a 40% reduction in US SO_2 emissions).

The United Kingdom's Central Electricity Generating Board (CEGB) meanwhile warned in 1983 that the United Kingdom faced a bill of £4 billion ($5.2 billion) and annual costs of £700 million if SO_2 emissions were to be reduced threefold. By 1984 it was talking of a total bill of £2 billion for a 30% reduction, an estimate dismissed by the *Guardian* as scare tactics. In 1980 the CEGB estimated that the cost of fitting FGD equipment to one new 2,000 MW power station was £250 million. In 1983 it put the cost at £150 million per station. By 1984 it was quoting a figure of £120 million. It has also variously put the cost to consumers in increased electricity rates at anything from 4% to 10%, and has warned of the dangers of increased unemployment.

These figures contrast dramatically with the conclusions of the 1982 OECD symposium, which heard evidence that the average costs for controlling emissions came to about 4% of total plant capital costs, and that operating costs would increase by about 2%. The simplest modifications, resulting in NO_x removal of 10–30%, would add no more than 1% to capital costs and 0.5% to running costs. Research and development in the United States and Japan meanwhile promise to reduce the costs of pollution control by 10–20% by the end of the decade, and by as much as a third in the long term. The LIMB process in particular could reduce the control costs for the low-sulphur coal by as much as 60% if it were commercialized successfully.

Pollution control is expensive – no one seriously questions this basic proposition. In the United States alone, existing pollution controls (which have had only limited success, see chapter 7) currently cost about $30 billion per year. The acid pollution controls proposed by President Bush in June 1989 would add an estimated $14–18 billion to the air pollution control budget. The costs of action are relatively easy to estimate; the costs of *inaction*, by contrast, are much less easily calculated. It is difficult to put a precise monetary value on acidified forests and lakes, dead animals and plants, reduced rural vistas, corroded buildings, or impaired human health. It is also difficult to be sure just how much of this damage is caused by acid pollution, and how much by other factors.

Against this background, the hard logic of conventional benefit-cost analysis seems all but useless. When it comes to calculating budgets, policy-makers prefer the kind of hard figures that are so elusive when it comes to acid pollution. This is one of the fundamental dilemmas created by the nature of environmental management and planning.

NOTES

1. Kash, Don E. and Robert W. Rycroft, *US Energy Policy: Crisis and Complacency* (Norman, Oklahoma: University of Oklahoma Press, 1984).
2. Wetstone, Gregory S. and Armin Rosencranz, *Acid Rain in Europe and North America: National Responses to an International Problem* (Washington DC: Environmental Law Institute, 1983).
3. See note 2.
4. Parker, L.B. and R.E. Trumbule, *Mitigating Acid Rain with Technology: Avoiding the Scrubbing-Switching Dilemma* (Washington, DC: Congressional Research Service, Library of Congress, 27 June 1983).
5. Gould, Roy, *Going Sour: Science and Politics of Acid Rain* (Boston: Birkhäuser, 1985); and US Office of Technology Assessment, *Acid Rain and Transported Air Pollutants: Implications for Public Policy* (Washington, DC: GPO,1984).
6. Regens, James L., and Robert W. Rycroft, *The Acid Rain Controversy* (Pittsburgh: University of Pittsburgh Press, 1988).
7. United States Office of Technology Assessment, *Acid Rain and Transported Air Pollutants: Implications for Public Policy* (Washington DC: Government Printing Office, 1984).
8. Kilgroe, J.D., "Coal cleaning for sulfur dioxide control." Paper to acid rain conference, Springfield, Virginia, April 1980.
9. *ENDS Report* 109, Environmental Data Service, February 1984.
10. Parker, L.B. and A. Kaufman, *Clean Coal Technology and Acid Rain Control: Birds of a Feather?* (Washington, DC: Congressional Research Service, Library of Congress, 23 October 1985).
11. CONCAWE, *SO₂ Emission Trends and Control Options for Western Europe* The Hague, 1982; and N. Elam and Trichem Consultants Ltd, *Present and Future Levels of Sulphur Dioxide Emissions in Northern Europe*, prepared for Swedish Ministry of Agriculture, Stockholm, 1979.
12. See note 11.
13. Parker and Trumbule 1983, see note 4.
14. Regens and Rycroft, see note 6.
15. UN Economic Commission for Europe, *Effects and Control of*

Transboundary Air Pollution, Air Pollution Studies No. 4, (New York: United Nations, 1987).

16. Regens and Rycroft, see note 6.
17. Anderson, Ian, "A coal gasification combined cycle power plant: new interest in coal combustion technology", in *Ambio* 16:1, 1987, pp. 64–5.
18. UN Economic Commission for Europe, *National Strategies and Policies for Air Pollution Abatement* (New York: United Nations, 1987).
19. Regens and Rycoft, see note 6.
20. Environmental Protection Agency, *Sulfur Emissions Control Technology and Waste Management* (Washington, DC: Office of Research and Development, May 1982).
21. US-Canada Work Group 3B, *Emissions, Costs and Engineering Assessment*, Final Report (Washington, DC: US Environmental Protection Agency, 1982).
22. *ENDS Report* 112, Environmental Data Service, May 1984.
23. Wetstone and Rosencranz, see note 2.
24. OECD, *Control Technology for Nitrogen Oxide Emissions From Stationary Sources* (London: HMSO, 1983).
25. House of Commons Written Answers, from Lynda Chalker, Under Secretary of State, Cols 431–2, 5 March 1984.
26. *ENDS Report* 119, Environmental Data Services, December 1984.
27. House of Lords Select Committee on the European Communities, *22nd Report: Air Pollution* (London: HMSO, 1984).
28. Leach, Gerald and others, *A Low Energy Strategy for the United Kingdom* (London: IIED, 1979).
29. Chandler, William U., *Energy Productivity: Key to Environmental Protection and Economic Progress* (Washington, DC: Worldwatch Paper No. 63, January 1985).
30. OECD, *Costs of Coal Pollution Abatement* (London: HMSO, 1983).

4. Acid Pollution as an International Issue

On 5 December 1952, a particularly nasty smog struck London. Londoners were used to fogs; indeed, the city was famous for the kinds of pea-soupers that lent so much Hollywood atmosphere to the exploits of Sherlock Holmes. In 1866, 1873 and 1918, winter fogs had caused excess death rates in the city of between 240 and 785. But the 1952 smog was much worse, and – more importantly – it captured media attention. It was so dense that a performance of *La Traviata* at Sadler's Wells had to be abandoned because the audience could not see the stage.[1]

On central London's road, visibility fell to 5 yards; on the Thames, ships came to a standstill; flights in and out of London were delayed. Worst of all, an estimated 4,000 people died from heart and lung ailments associated with the effects of the smog, and many more fell ill. Californian environmental engineer Michael Hoffmann has estimated that the smog had a pH of between 1.4 and 1.9, making it almost as acidic as battery acid.[2]

Campaigners had been working without much success since the late nineteenth century to reduce pollution in London. Now, suddenly, policy-makers and the public began to take notice. Following the smog, smoke control regulations were rapidly tightened, and the world's first piece of comprehensive national air pollution legislation – the Clean Air Act – was passed in July 1956. The emission of "dark smoke" was prohibited, new furnaces had to be designed to be as smokeless as possible, local authorities were given the power to declare smoke-control zones, and grants were made available to convert domestic fireplaces so that Britons could burn smokeless fuel. Three decades later, the benefits were obvious: levels of grit, smoke and dust in the atmosphere had been greatly reduced, London had many more hours of sunlight (especially in winter), and buildings like the Houses of Parliament, Westminster Abbey and St Paul's Cathedral were being cleaned of centuries of grime.

The policy response had begun, and attempts to control local air pollution in the United Kingdom and other industrial countries in the 1950s included building tall smokestacks at many power stations and factories. These curbed local pollution, but they also dispersed much of the pollution to the winds, thereby affecting areas further away from the source of emissions. In other words, local pollution was controlled at the expense of making acid pollution an increasingly international problem. The transnational nature of air pollution had been suspected as early as the 1880s; research in the 1950s now confirmed that pollutants could be carried great distances.

In parts of Sweden, downwind of the major industrial centres of the United Kingdom and West Germany, the acidity of rain doubled between 1956 and 1965.[3] Swedish concern moved Sverker Astrom, the Swedish ambassador to the UN, to suggest the convening of an international conference to discuss environmental problems.[4] The result was the UN Conference on the Human Environment, held in Stockholm in 1972. Sweden's case study for the conference described the problem of transboundary air pollution, and asserted that increases in the acidity of Swedish rain were caused by pollutants from the burning of fossil fuel in neighbouring countries.[5] The estimated costs of this pollution (in liming of lakes and farmland, losses from reduced forest growth, and reduced crop production) was put at Kr87 million per annum. Despite some scepticism, the study contributed to the acceptance of Principle 21 of the Declaration of the Stockholm conference. This pointed out that states have an obligation to ensure that activities carried out in one country do not cause environmental damage in other countries, or to the global commons.

Prompted by the work of Svante Odén and others, a veritable flood of research now emerged from Sweden and Norway, illustrating the links between acid pollution and forest decline, changes in the chemistry of soils, increased acidity in forests and lakes, and decreases in freshwater fish populations. In 1972, the Norwegian Council for Scientific and Industrial Research, the Agricultural

Research Council of Norway, and the Ministry of the Environment launched the SNSF Project (the Norwegian Interdisciplinary Research Programme) with an annual budget of $2 million.

Research took on a broader perspective in April 1972 (two months before the Stockholm conference), when the OECD launched a four-year study (the Co-operative Technical Programme to Measure the Long-Range Transport of Air Pollutants, or LRTAP project) in its eleven European member countries. The aim was to reach a common understanding about the causes and effects of sulphur emissions, of possible transport within Europe, and of possible deposition and adverse effects hundreds or even thousands of kilometres from the source. Nearly eighty observation stations were set up to take samples of the sulphur content of air and precipitation. The results, published in 1977,[6] provided convincing evidence of the chemistry and transport of acid pollution, and backed up many of the assertions made by the Scandinavian scientists. Airborne pollutants could and were being blown across borders. It was made clear which countries were net senders and net receivers of pollutants. In five of the eleven participating countries (Finland, Norway, Sweden, Austria and Switzerland), more than half the total deposition of sulphur was estimated to come from foreign sources.[7] James MacNeill, later OECD environment director, observed that the survey had shown that "precipitation in one country was, without doubt, being measurably affected by emissions from sources in other countries". The LRTAP project also revealed that the problems were not confined to Western Europe. On the contrary, they involved all European countries north of the Alps.

In North America, meanwhile, a continent-wide precipitation chemistry network had operated between 1960 and 1966. But scientists worked in isolation and relative obscurity, and there were no continuing records; as late as 1982 congressional committees were hearing complaints that precipitation research was inadequate.[8] Canadian concerns about acid pollution grew during the 1970s as fish populations were found to be declining in more and more lakes in southern Ontario and Nova Scotia. Stimulated by the work of Scandinavian scientists, experimental studies began in the United States, and in 1975 the US Forest Service sponsored an international symposium on acid pollution and forests. A Canadian sampling network was established in 1976, and in 1977 the US Council on Environmental Quality (CEQ) launched an assessment programme that provided the basis for President Carter's 1978 Initiative on Acid Precipitation. The US National Acid Deposition Program (NADP) was founded in 1978, and now maintains a network of sampling stations throughout the country.

The first bilateral research programme was set up between the United States and Canada in 1978[9], and within two years had documented the transboundary flow of air pollutants, showing that eleven times more NOx and two to four times more SO_2 were transported from the United States to Canada than vice versa.[10] Also in 1978, congress passed a resolution calling bilateral discussions with Canada. In 1979, a Joint Statement on Transboundary Air Quality was issued, expressing "common determination to reduce or prevent transboundary air pollution which injures health or property",[11] a "determination" which was to seem increasingly hollow to Canadians as they wrestled with the caution of the Reagan administration. In 1980, a Memorandum of Intent (MOI) was signed by the two countries, agreeing to develop a bi-lateral agreement on trans-boundary air pollution, including "the already serious problem of acid rain." The MOI emphasized the need for domestic pollution control policies, but there was little sign during the remainder of the Reagan presidency of a commitment by the United States to strengthen those policies (see chapter 7).

The Convention on Long-Range Transboundary Air Pollution

It became increasingly obvious during the 1970s that air pollution was an international problem. Yet despite the work of the 1972–77 OECD project, which provided the first independent verification of Scandinavian charges that imported sulphur was behind its acidification problems, the Scandinavians still found themselves virtually alone during the mid-1970s in promoting international contacts. The change came with the 1975 Helsinki Conference on Security and Co-operation, when Soviet leader Leonid Brezhnev suggested that attempts should be made to reach agreement on three pan-European problems: energy, transport and environment. Energy and transport were fraught with political and economic problems, the former because of strategic concerns, and the latter because of West German concerns that the Eastern bloc would demand greater access to the Rhine-Main-Danube canal.[12]

The environment was the least politically charged of the three options, so Sweden and Norway used the opportunity to propose air pollution as the major theme of discussions. An administrative body was needed because the OECD had no powers of enforcement, and neither Sweden nor Norway were members of the EC. This left the UN Economic Commission for Europe (ECE), the regional UN body for Europe. It is based in Geneva and has the major advantage of membership by thirty-four European countries from East and West.

The ECE accepted the project, and negotiations began in 1977. The substance of the exercise was to elaborate a convention on long-range transboundary air pollution to be signed by all European states, the United States and Canada. Sweden and Norway pressed for a tough convention that would call for a halt to increases in SO_2 emissions (the so-called "standstill" clause), together with a "rollback" clause that specified SO_2 abatement by fixed percentage levels of up to 50%. Exceptions were to be made for countries that had either already implemented abatement measures (such as the Netherlands) or those in a relatively early stage of industrial development (such as Ireland). But a number of countries objected to legally binding controls. The opposition was led by the United Kingdom and West Germany, which were not even prepared at that stage to commit themselves to the standstill clause.

After further negotiations, the United Kingdom finally accepted the convention in the belief that plans for an expansion of its nuclear power programme would help reduce sulphur emissions. Diplomatic pressure from France, Sweden and Norway meanwhile brought West Germany around.[13] The final convention consisted of little more than a general obligation on each contracting party to "endeavour to limit and, as far as possible, gradually reduce and prevent air pollution including long-range transboundary air pollution." This was to be done with the use of the "best available technology which is economically feasible in new and retrofitted plants". These terms, "best available technology" and "economically feasible" (the latter included at the insistence of West Germany), were subsequently given wide and loose interpretation.

The Convention on Long-Range Transboundary Air Pollution was signed in Geneva in November 1979 by thirty-five countries, including the United Kingdom, the United States, and West and East Germany. It was the first environmental agreement involving all the nations of East and West Europe and North America. Signature of a treaty, however, imposes no legal obligations. It simply commits a signatory (as an act of good faith) not to do anything to frustrate the objects of the treaty until the signatory state makes it clear that it does not intend to become a party.[14] A state only commits itself legally when it ratifies a treaty, having had time to think through all the implications. So a resolution was adopted at Geneva requesting the signatories to start implementing the provisions of the convention on a voluntary basis, starting with sulphur emissions, until such time as the convention could enter into force. By March 1983, the twenty-four ratifications needed to bring the convention into force had been collected. By March 1985, thirty countries and the European Community had ratified.

The convention was initially criticized for its lack of power, and even dismissed as an excuse for doing nothing about large emissions. Yet it had symbolic value in that countries from Eastern and Western Europe, the Soviet Union and the United States all signed the document. Given the cooling of East-West relations in the early 1980s, it is likely that no convention at all would have been possible a year or so after the Geneva meeting.

The convention deals not only with SO_2, but with other sulphur, nitrogen and chlorine compounds, polycyclic aromatic hydrocarbons, heavy metals, particles, and other substances. So it could in the long run prove useful in efforts to deal with pollutants other than SO_2 (including NO_x). It also strengthened the key European data gathering network – the Co-operative Programme for Monitoring and Evaluation of Long-Range Transmission of Air Pollutants in Europe (EMEP). EMEP, designed to provide information on the transboundary flow of air pollutants, has been operating since 1978 with sixty stations in twenty countries in East and West. Set up originally under the auspices of the ECE, EMEP is now run by the Executive Body of the Convention.

Stockholm 1982: a change of heart

The lukewarm response to the convention by some of Europe's biggest polluters, and the prevailing lack of public awareness about acid pollution, encouraged Sweden to use the tenth anniversary of the 1972 Stockholm conference as a publicity vehicle. Lacking the requisite twenty-four ratifications, the convention had not yet entered into force, so Sweden invited all the original signatories to the convention to the Conference on the Acidification of the Environment, held in Stockholm in June 1982. This conference was held in two stages: a scientific and technical meeting, and a ministerial meeting.

The first meeting, attended by experts representing themselves rather than their countries or governments, scrutinized all the scientific evidence of the causes, transport and effects of transboundary air pollutants, and the technical material available on strategies and methods (including costs) for the control of emissions. They arrived at three main conclusions:

1. Non-natural sulphur and nitrogen compounds were primarily responsible for acid deposition, and a decrease in emissions over a large industrialized region would lead to an "approximately proportionate" decrease in acid deposition, and a "positive improvement" in stressed aquatic systems.
2. A "threshold value" of 0.5 grammes of sulphur per square metre per year for sulphur deposition was agreed; above that level, sensitive aquatic ecosystems would begin to be harmed.
3. Technology was commercially available that could radically reduce emissions of air pollutants. The fact that improved technologies may emerge in the future did not justify waiting and delaying the use of existing technology.

The ministerial meeting adopted these conclusions, and some of their own. The ministers declared:

o that acidification problems were serious and that even if total deposition was not allowed to rise, damage to soil and water would get worse unless prompt action was taken within the framework of the convention. This action should include: (1) the elaboration of concerted programmes for the reduction first of SO_2 emissions, and then of NO_x, and (2) the use of the best economically available control methods, including flue gas desulphurization (FGD), low-sulphur fuels, desulphurization of fuels, and new combustion technology.

○ that the "tall-chimney principle" was outdated and should be abandoned. Whatever pollution load tall chimneys may have removed from the local environment, the associated long-range, transboundary pollution was unacceptable.[15]

These were positive conclusions. International agreement had been reached, and demands had been made for concrete measures. Any dismay over the absence from the conference of the Soviet Union, Poland, and Czechoslovakia was offset by a dramatic policy about-face announced by West Germany. The first alarming reports of forest damage in West Germany had by then begun to appear, and the growing momentum of the Greens (they won their first Landtag seats in 1981 and their first Bundestag seats in March 1983) was beginning to change the West German political agenda. This was encouraging Helmut Schmidt's Social Democratic government to adopt increasingly green policies (see chapter 6). It had become obvious that a position against acid pollution controls was no longer tenable. The West Germans now declared their intention to halve their SO_2 emissions in ten years and to raise the question of the international environment at the next world economic summit; they pointed out that global success could only be achieved by concerted international action.

Ottawa and Munich 1984: the birth of the 30% Club

Conferences seldom bring about radical changes, but the 1982 Stockholm conference had one major effect: the process of ratifying the ECE convention was speeded up. Within months, all the EC countries had ratified, and the convention came into force in early 1983. Another substantive result was the Nordic proposal for a mutual 30% reduction of SO_2 emissions in the ten years from 1983 to 1993, calculated from emission levels in 1980. This proposal was put to the signatories at the first meeting of the Executive Body of the Convention in Geneva in June 1983. Immediate support came from Canada, Austria, Switzerland and West Germany. The Nordic proposal was accompanied by one from Austria, Switzerland and West Germany calling for NO_x reductions, but this was strongly opposed by the East European bloc, and ended up as a first step towards integrating NO_x with the agenda of EMEP.

The Nordic 30% proposal was rejected by the EB; Western countries (notably the United Kingdom, France and the United States) joined with the Eastern European countries in their opposition. What came out of the discussion was "a recognition of the need to decrease effectively the total annual emissions of sulphur compounds, or their transboundary fluxes, by 1993–95 using 1980 emission levels as the basis for calculation". The term "transboundary flux" (the volume of SO_2 that crosses national borders) was coined by the Soviet Union and its Eastern European allies to support their view that only pollutants actually sent across borders should be dealt with in international co-operation. What happened inside a country, they argued, was strictly an internal matter. The East European countries agreed to co-operate in setting up air quality and precipitation monitoring stations and pooling the data thus gathered, but refused to make emission data available, arguing that they would reveal sensitive economic and energy information. Limiting its commitment to "transboundary fluxes" works in favour of the Soviet Union because prevailing westerly winds mean that most Soviet emissions do not affect neighbouring countries.

Impatient at the lack of progress under the terms of the ECE convention, and convinced that rapid and big reductions in SO_2 emissions were needed, representatives from ten of the countries that supported the Nordic concept of a 30% reduction in SO_2 emissions met in Ottawa in March 1984 to sign their own agreement. The minimum requirement was an undertaking to reduce SO_2 emissions by 30% by 1993 (using 1980 figures as the baseline) – hence the name of "30% Club". France, West Germany, Canada and Norway went further by committing themselves to 50% reductions (that of France to be achieved by 1990), and Denmark and the Netherlands agreed to aim for a 40% reduction. The remaining original members were Austria, Finland, Sweden and Switzerland. The Ottawa conference also, for the first time, put NO_x high on the international

Table 4.1: Original members of the 30% Club

Date of accession	Reduction by 30% by 1993	Reduction by more than 30%
March 1984	Finland	
March 1984	Sweden	
March 1984	Switzerlandd	
June 1984	Belgium	
June 1984	Bulgaria	
June 1984	Byelorussia	
June 1984	E. Germany	
June 1984	Liechtenstein	
June 1984	Luxembourg	
June 1984	Soviet Union	
June 1984	Ukrainia	
Sept 1984	Czechoslovakia	
Sept 1984	Italy	
April 1985	Hungary	
March 1984		Austria (50% by 1993)
March 1984		Canada (50% by 1994)
March 1984		Denmark (40% by 1995)
March 1984		W.Germany (50% by 1993)
March 1984		Norway (50% by 1994)
March 1984		France (50% by 1990)
March 1984		Netherlands (40% by 1995)

agenda by declaring that the participating countries would "take measures to decrease effectively the total annual emissions of nitrogen oxides from stationary and mobile sources as soon as possible and at the latest by 1993".

A second major international conference – the Multilateral Conference on the Environment – was held in Munich from 24 to 27 June 1984, with the partial aim of encouraging more countries to join the 30% Club. The conference was attended by environment ministers from the countries within the convention. It requested that the EB should, as a matter of priority at its second meeting in September 1984, adopt a proposal for a specific agreement on the reduction of annual national sulphur emissions (or their "transboundary fluxes") by 1993 at the latest. It was also decided that total annual emissions (or "trans-boundary fluxes") of NO_x from all sources should be effectively reduced by 1995, considering that several countries had already committed themselves to such reductions at an earlier date. It was also recommended that the EB include NO_x in its work programme.

Given the strong opposition at the first EB meeting against even mentioning NO_x problems, these decisions were another breakthrough. But the United States still remained outside the fold. The Canadian environment minister had said in Ottawa that if the Americans did not go to Munich, the Soviet Union would take advantage of the opportunity to appear co-operative on pollution controls and reap the public relations benefits; for that reason, the United States had to provide international leadership on acid rain. Although the Americans went to Munich, they said they could agree to no specific NO_x reductions.

In December 1983 the Commission of the EC proposed a Council Directive on large emissions reductions in the member countries: 60% reductions of SO_2, 40% of NO_x and 40% of dust. Traditional thermal power stations were the main target, and the reductions were set for 1995. These stations account for more that 80% of SO_2 emissions and 40% of NO_x emissions within the EC. This proposal was inspired partly by new West German legislation on air pollution from power stations. The Commission calculated that additional costs for reductions would amount to less than 10% of production costs. The annual costs of damage from acid pollution are at least comparable, if not higher. The OECD estimated the annual costs to the EC of acid deposition to be between $50 and $65 billion (35% of the Community's GNP).

The Commission also suggested that all member countries should switch to unleaded petrol from 1989, but that it should be up to each country to introduce unleaded petrol whenever they wished, beginning in 1986. The Commission proposed that catalytic converters (US standards) should be fully introduced to all member countries by 1995 at the latest. Individual countries would again be free to introduce regulations earlier if they wanted (see chapter

6 for more details on EC legislation).

Further evidence of a new level of interest in the global implications of acid pollution came in December 1984, when environment ministers from six of the seven Western Economic Summit countries met in London to discuss priority environmental issues. The meeting (attended by the United Kingdom, Canada, West Germany, Italy, Japan, the United States and the European Commission) followed an agreement at the June 1984 economic summit that efforts should be made to identify environmental issues on which there was a need for increased international co-operation. There was no formal agenda, but acid deposition was at the top of the list in the letter of invitation sent to environment ministers by then UK Environment Minister Patrick Jenkin.

In a statement following the meeting, Jenkin said it had stressed the "indivisibility of environmental and economic policies," and agreed that there was an urgent need for increased international co-operation on long-term global environmental issues, using existing institutions. These should be given "unambiguous priorities and effective channels for the implementation of decisions." Carl-Dieter Spranger, parliamentary state secretary in the West German Interior Ministry, told the meeting that his government considered the environment "the most important policy field next to the safeguarding of peace." The West German government, he said, had learned that "a flourishing economy and effective environmental protection are dependent on each other.... New low-pollution production processes and environmentally compatible products are a chance of combining the ecologically necessary with the economically reasonable".

Helsinki 1985: the convention is given teeth

The third EB meeting, at Helsinki in July 1985, finally saw the convention given substance. At the second EB meeting in the previous September, work had begun on drawing up a protocol on the reduction of sulphur emissions along the lines of the original Nordic proposal at the first EB meeting. A draft was ready in February 1985, and the protocol – which binds its signatories to a 30% reduction of SO_2 at source by 1993 on 1980 levels (the same

Table 4.2: Reductions in SO$_2$ emissions

	Most recent year for which figures available	%change since 1980	projected% change on 1980 figures	
			1990	1995
Austria	1985	−52		−72*
Switzerland	1986	−50	−54	
France	1985	−48	−49	
Sweden	1985	−44		−68
Luxembourg	1985	−43	−57	
Belgium	1984	−42		−32
Finland	1985	−37		−54
Ireland	1985	−37		+15
Netherlands	1983	−35		−51
Norway	1985†	−29		−50†
West Germany	1985	−25		−66
Denmark	1985	−25		−48
UK	1984	−24	−27‡	
Canada	1983	−20		
Italy	1983	−17		
USSR	1985	−13	−30	
Hungary	1985	−13		−30
USA	1983	−10		
Greece	1983	−10		
Czechoslovakia	1986	−2		−31
East Germany	1983	0		
Spain	1983	0	−6	
Poland	1985	+5	+20	
Bulgaria*	1983	+10		
Portugal	1983	+15		
Yugoslavia	1984	+53		

* = estimated   † = preliminary   ‡ = planned

Source: calculated from figures in United Nations, *National Strategies and Policies for Air Pollution Abatement* (New York: United Nations, 1987).

terms as the 30% Club) – was opened for signature at Helsinki. It was immediately signed by the twenty-one members of the 30% Club. By September 1987, sixteen of those countries had ratified the protocol, finally bringing it into force.

Hopes that more countries – including possibly even the United Kingdom – might have used the occasion to join the 30% Club came to nought. The United Kingdom lamely explained that while it had (by its own calculations) gone much of the way and reduced SO_2 emissions by 25% since 1980, it could not be sure that it would be able to achieve the remaining 5% reduction by 1993.[16] The American delegation claimed major progress, reporting that the United States had reduced SO_2 emissions by 28% between 1973 and 1983, and by 10% between 1980 and 1983; however, it could not sign the protocol because scientific uncertainty made it impossible to design a cost-effective programme of additional SO_2 controls. "While we do not insist on 100% certitude," said Richard Benedick, head of the US delegation, "our policy-makers must have the confidence that any proposed solution will in fact solve the problems of acid deposition." If the weight of evidence ultimately confirmed that further SO_2 reductions were needed "to protect the environment", he assured the conference, the United States would consider "additional measures", including a retrofit programme.[17]

Poland, while admitting that sulphur concentrations and trans-boundary fluxes had increased, argued that the technology needed to control emissions would not be available until the 1990s, and suggested that the state of the Polish economy precluded anything more than the short-term aim of stabilizing SO_2 emissions. The second stage (no time-table was given) was a 30% reduction. It could not therefore sign the protocol.[18]

Amsterdam 1986 and Sofia 1988: progress on NO_x control

All the countries represented at Helsinki were unanimous in their support of the EMEP programme and of the need to begin work on the next stage in giving the LRTAP convention more substance: a protocol on NO_x. But negotiations on reductions in NO_x have proved more complicated than those

Table 4.3: Reductions in NO_x emissions

	Most recent year for which figures available	% change since 1980	projected % change on 1980 figures 1990	projected % change on 1980 figures 1995
Belgium	1984	−13		−3
UK	1984	−12	+10	
Finland	1983	−11		+9
France*	1985	−9		
Czechoslovakia	1986	−9		−21
Sweden	1985	−7		−27
West Germany	1985	−6		−45
Denmark	1985	−5		+29
Switzerland	1986	−5		−25#
USA	1983	−4		+2
Luxembourg	1985	−4	−35	
Netherlands	1983	−2	−6	
Italy†	1983	−1		
Austria	1985	0		−31
Ireland	1985	+2		+83
Canada	1983	+3		
USSR	1985	+5		
Hungary‡	1986	+11		
Portugal	1983	+16		
Greece	1983	+18		

No figures available for East Germany, Romania, Turkey, Yugoslavia, Spain, Poland, Hungary, Norway, Bulgaria

* does not include 700,000 tonnes from agricultural activities
†figures represent upper limit of emissions
‡preliminary figures
#1993

Sources: calculated from figures in United Nations, *National Strategies and Policies for Air Pollution Abatement* (New York: United Nations, 1987).

on SO_2. There are no broadly accepted international air quality or emission standards for NO_x, there are big differences in the domestic structure of industry and road transport in ECE member countries, and the Eastern European countries oppose NO_x controls, citing scientific uncertainty about its effects.[19]

At the International Conference on Acidification and its Policy Implications, held in Amsterdam in May 1986, delegates took up the call made at Helsinki for accelerated research on NO_x.[20] But it was another two years before a draft agreement had been reached, calling on member nations to freeze NO_x emissions at 1987 levels by 1994. The United States argued that it had already cut its NO_x emissions, and that countries should be allowed to choose any year as the baseline. A compromise was then suggested, allowing countries to choose any year as the baseline provided they capped transboundary flows at 1987 levels within ten years.

At an ECE meeting at Sofia in November 1988, twenty-five countries finally signed the protocol. The twelve European Community countries went further by agreeing to reduce NO_x emission by 30% by 1998, in line with the June 1988 EC directive (see chapter 6). Agreement on the protocol marked an important new step in progress towards curbing acid pollution. Even though the United States – the world's biggest producer of NO_x – did not agree to the 30% reduction, it signed the protocol. This marked the first time that it had entered into a binding agreement to reduce NO_x and the first time it had made a binding agreement to Canada to reduce acid rain.

A decade of progress: 1979–1989

November 1989 marks the tenth anniversary of the signing of the ECE convention. Just how much was achieved in the first decade of acid pollution diplomacy? The commitment made by so many countries in 1979 and 1984 to reduce SO_2 and NO_x pollution was met with a certain amount of scepticism, particularly by the countries that held back from ratifying the ECE convention or joining the 30% Club. Until its about-face in 1988, the United Kingdom defended itself by saying that its decision not to agree to SO_2 controls was more honest than the decisions of those countries who had ratified the ECE convention with little prospect of meeting its terms. In fact, progress on reducing SO_2 and NO_x has generally been very good (see tables 4.2 and 4.3).

As regards SO_2, the most spectacular progress has come from Austria, Switzerland and France, which have already cut their emissions in half, and from Sweden, Luxembourg and Belgium, which have achieved reductions of more than 40%. Austria halved its emissions in just five years (1980–1985), and plans a 72% reduction – bigger than any other country – by 1995. Six of the ten original members of the 30% Club had already met the Club terms by 1985, eight years ahead of schedule. Out of the total membership of twenty-one countries, only the Eastern bloc countries are lagging behind. In fact, their story there makes worrying reading. The European Soviet Union and Hungary reduced their emissions by 13% between 1980 and 1985, and are both confident of meeting the 30% goal on time, but Czechoslovakia managed only a 2% reduction between 1980 and 1986, and emissions in Bulgaria actually grew by 10% between 1980 and 1983.

As regards NO_x, reductions have so far been much slower. Belgium, the United Kingdom and Finland have so far achieved the biggest reductions, but much bigger reductions are projected for West Germany, Austria, Luxembourg and Sweden in the period 1990–1995.

So the first ten years of international acid pollution controls have produced a treaty and two protocols, which between them have helped encourage major reductions in SO_2 and NO_x. Whether these reductions have been big enough or quick enough to save Europe's forests, croplands, lakes, rivers, fisheries, buildings and people from more damage remains to be seen. The significance of the ECE convention in paving the way for other environmental treaties – like the 1985 convention on the ozone layer, and a possible future agreement on global warming – also remains to be seen. Finally, there is the problem of acid pollution in less developed countries. Will agreement be reached as easily in countries desperate to develop their industrial base, and too poor to afford emission controls?

NOTES

1. *The Times*, 9 December 1952.

2. *New Scientist*, 9 February 1984.

3. Lundholm, B., "Interactions between oceans and terrestrial systems", in Singer, S.F. (ed.), *Global Effects of Environmental Pollution* (Dordrecht, the Netherlands: Reidel, 1970).

4. McCormick, John, *The Global Environmental Movement: Reclaiming Paradise* (London: Belhaven Press, 1989).

5. Bolin, Bert, and others "Sweden's case study for the United Nations Conference on the Human Environment: air pollution across national boundaries" (Stockholm: Norstadt & Sons, 1972).

6. OECD Environmental Directorate, *The OECD Programme on Long Range Transport of Air Pollutants: Summary Report* (Paris: OECD, 1977).

7. See note 6.

8. Cowling, Ellis B., "Acid precipitation in historical perspective", in *Environmental Science and Technology* 16:2 January 1982, pp. 110A–22A.

9. Bilateral Research Consultation Group on the Long-Range Transport of Air Pollutants, *The Long Range Transport of Air Pollutants Problem in North America: A Preliminary Overview* (Washington, DC: Canadian Embassy, Public Affairs Division, 1979). Second Report published in 1980.

10. Altshuller and McBean, 1979, quoted in Cowling, see note 8.

11. Wetstone, Gregory S. and Armin Rosencranz, *Acid Rain in Europe and North America: National Responses to an International Problem* (Washington, DC: Environmental Law Institute, 1983).

12. See note 11.

13. See note 11.

14. Lyster, Simon, *International Wildlife Law* (Cambridge: Grotius Publications, 1985).

15. Swedish Ministry of Agriculture, *The 1982 Stockholm Conference on Acidification of the Environment* (Stockholm: Departementens Reprocentral, 1982).

16. UK report to the Third Meeting of the Executive Body of the Convention on Long-Range Transboundary Air Pollution, Helsinki, July 1985, unpublished.

17. US report to the Third Meeting of the Executive Body of the Convention on Long-Range Transboundary Air Pollution, Helsinki, July 1985, unpublished.

18. Polish report to the Third Meeting of the Executive Body of the Convention on Long-Range Transboundary Air Pollution, Helsinki, July 1985, unpublished.

19. Rosencranz, Armin, "The ECE convention of 1979 on long-range transboundary air pollution," in *American Journal of International Law* 75, 1981.

20. "Conference says abatement programs have not reduced acidification enough", in *International Environment Reporter* 9:6, 1986, pp. 183–4.

5. The United Kingdom – Thatcherism and the Environment

In a September 1988 speech to the Royal Society in London, Prime Minister Margaret Thatcher stunned environmentalists by declaring that protection of the environment and the balance of nature was "one of the great challenges of the twentieth century". Only three months before, the Thatcher administration had approved the terms of the 1988 EC directive on large combustion plants, committing the United Kingdom to a 60% reduction in SO_2 emissions by the year 2003. After years of intransigence and criticism from most of Europe, the United Kingdom had not only agreed to reduce emissions, but had gone well beyond the demands of either the ECE Convention or the 30% Club. This was a startling reversal of policy. Thatcherism had become synonymous with opposition to regulation, yet Thatcher now seemed willing to agree to regulation if the proof about a threat to the environment (or, perhaps, the weight of opposition) was sufficiently convincing. "The environment has finally arrived as one of the big political issues", noted Martin Jacques in *The Sunday Times*. "At last British politics has turned a shade of green. . .Nothing will be quite the same again".[1]

Not everyone was convinced by the prime minister's words, however, and many environmentalists accused her of electoral opportunism. There had been very little in her record to suggest the possibility of a true commitment to green policies. Her apparent conversion came at the end of almost a decade of growing pressure from inside and outside the country. Long after all her European partners had acceded to the terms of the ECE convention and the 30% Club, Thatcher refused to acknowledge that acid rain was a problem. As the debate progressed, she found herself increasingly isolated. Not only did senior Tory backbenchers question her intransigence, but so did senior members of her government and the Department of the Environment. (It was long understood that her moderate environment minister, William Waldegrave – who was shifted to the state housing portfolio in 1987 and thence to the foreign office – and his chief scientist, Martin Holdgate, were more than sympathetic to the demands of the United Kingdom's neighbouring countries.)

The United Kingdom's position had by turns puzzled and infuriated its European neighbours. On the one hand, the United Kingdom has a long and creative history of action on the environment. Robert Angus Smith – a Scottish chemist – was the first to identify the link between industrial emissions and acid pollution. The 1863 Alkali Act was the first air pollution law in the world. London's Battersea power station, opened in 1929, was the first installation in the world fitted with an operational scrubber. London was one of the first cities in the world to respond to the effects of smog and to impose a successful smog control programme. And the 1956 Clean Air Act was the world's first comprehensive air pollution law, providing the model for similar legislation elsewhere, including the United States.

Yet during the 1980s, the United Kingdom perversely refused to commit itself to the terms either of the ECE convention or of the 30% Club, despite the fact that it was the biggest emitter of SO_2 in Western Europe (and the fourth biggest in the world); despite mounting evidence of acid damage to UK forests, lakes, rivers, wildlife, crops and buildings; despite mounting pressure on Thatcher from scientists, other EC governments, pressure groups, and members of her own party in the UK and European parliaments. But the 1988 policy reversals capped a steady change of attitude. The Central Electricity Generating Board (CEGB), long the most vocal opponent to emission controls, had moderated its stance since 1986, and in 1988 agreed to spend £1.2 million in ten years to reduce emissions from its power stations. Thatcher, after turning down previous requests for emission controls from the Department of the Environment, agreed first to a limited control programme,[2] and then to meeting the terms of the EC directive.

The combined weight of public, political and scientific opinion must have played an important role in this change of heart. Perhaps the final straw was the revelation by a 1987 Europe-wide forest survey that the United Kingdom had the highest percentage of damaged forests in Europe.[3] Thatcher's September 1988 speech seemed to mark a new and more open attitude to the growing weight of scientific evidence on acid pollution. Combined with the recent restructuring of the United Kingdom's pollution control activities (including for the first time the setting of air-quality standards and emission limits) and signs that it was increasingly prepared to meet its obligations under the EC's environmental legislation, the trend seems to be towards a more rational environmental policy. It has been many years in the making.

Emissions and damage

The United Kingdom produces about 3.5 million tonnes of SO_2 per year (1984 figures), making it the fourth biggest producer in the world. It also produces about 1.7 million tonnes of NO_x, making it one of the five biggest producers in the world.[4] It derives 92% of its energy needs from fossil fuels and most of the balance from nuclear power. Most of that energy comes from coal-fired power stations, which are in turn the major producers of SO_2 (see Table 5.1).

Robert Angus Smith confirmed the earliest damage from acid rain in the United Kingdom more than 130 years ago, but a complete picture of the extent of the damage is still emerging. According to a 1984 report by the government's Warren Spring Laboratory, the acidity of UK rain varies from pH 4.7–4.4 in the west to 4.3–4.1 in the east.[5] The report noted that parts of Cumbria and the west central highlands and southern uplands of Scotland were receiving the largest inputs of acidity, and that the amount of acid deposited was "of the same order as regions of Scandinavia and North America." The report found that the most acidic rain was associated with winds crossing the large industrial regions of the United Kingdom and Europe, while the cleanest rain was associated with winds coming from the North Atlantic.

The report dealt mainly with measurements of acidity in rainfall in the United Kingdom, and said little about its possible adverse effects. It did however reach the following conclusions:

○ The United Kingdom's rain is acid-polluted: it is commonly 100–150 times more acid than unpolluted rain, and in one case (at Bush, Scotland) more than 600 times more acidic than normal. Sulphur accounts for 70% of the acidity in UK rainfall, and nitrates for the remaining 30%
○ Other countries account for only 11% of all acidity in UK rainfall, although much of the deposition in the north-west United Kingdom may originate in Europe.

Table 5.1: Sources of SO_2 and NO_x in the UK

	SO_2 (thousand tonnes)			
	1972	%	1982	%
Power stations	2 870	51	2 650	66
Other ind/agric	1 750	31	760	19
Refineries	260	5	210	5
Domestic	370	6	200	5
Commercial/pub serv	310	5	170	4
Road transport	60	1	50	1
Rail transport	20	>1	10	>1
TOTAL	5 640	100	4 050	100

	NO_x (thousand tonnes)			
	1972	%	1982	%
Power stations	731	42	769	46
Road vehicles:				
petrol-engined	262	15	318	19
diesel-engined	158	9	172	10
Commercial/industrial	470	27	309	19
Domestic	51	3	51	3
Railways	48	3	35	2
Incineration and agric burning	8	>1	12	>1
TOTAL	1 728	100	1 666	100

Source: Warren Spring Laboratory, Department of Trade and Industry.

- Acidity comes in short bursts. For example, 30% of the acidity in rain falling at Goonhilly in Cheshire in 1980 fell in five days (2.7% of all wet days), with 50% falling in just ten days.
- Urban areas may suffer significantly higher acidities, for example, Norwich 94% in excess, Glasgow 41%, and Nottingham 20% (the report excluded urban sites and those near industry from its data base).
- Dry deposition of sulphur, which is difficult to measure because it enters (and damages) plants as fine gas or particles, is up to three times as acid as wet deposition in parts of the United Kingdom (especially south, east and central England). This may acidify wetlands (such as new forest pools, bogs) and damage crops.

Acid damage is undoubtedly affecting many parts of the country. The areas at greatest risk are those in which soils or bedrock have limited buffering capacity, notably parts of Wales, Scotland and the Lake District. Research on acidification in the Lake District dates back to the 1950s.[6] More recently, detailed research has been carried out in the lochs of Galloway in Scotland. As early as 1978, several lochs in the region were found to have had pH changes comparable to those of lakes in Norway and Sweden.[7] The Forestry Commission was sufficiently perturbed by the early results of a ten-year research programme by the Ministry of Agriculture, Fisheries and Food (MAFF) to begin liming lochs in the region in 1982. More recently, analysis of diatoms (skeletal remains of tiny algae) by researchers from University College London has provided compelling evidence that many of the lochs have become sharply more acidic in the last century, and that the change began just as air pollutants first began to reach the region. This puts into question the conventional wisdom that many lochs became acidic when farmers began clearing mountain forests 5,000 years ago, setting off acidification in upland soils.[8]

A 1983 report for the Welsh Water Authority pointed out that acidification had resulted in many of the upland streams, rivers and lakes draining afforested catchments in Dyfed and Gwynedd (south-west and north-west Wales respectively) becoming unable to support natural fish populations. In the river Tywi in mid-Wales, native brown trout had not been able to survive the combined effects of acidity and increased aluminium concentrations in water draining from conifer forests in the area. The Berwyn catchment in north Wales was too acidic even to support the American brook char, a fish introduced specifically to cope with the acid.[9]

Conifer plantations were abandoned in the Pennines as early as the 1930s because of high SO_2 levels.[10] More recently, there has been evidence of forest damage to trees in the Lake District.[11] A 1984 survey made by Joachim Puhe, a German forestry expert, on the invitation of the Scottish branch of Friends of the Earth, concluded that about 65% of the sites examined showed signs of damage from air pollution. Affected species included Scots pine, Norway spruce, Sitka spruce, Douglas fir and hardwoods (beech), all of which can be considered commercial forest species. Areas around the Lake District and the Forest of Dean were particularly affected.[12] Puhe's visit finally embarrassed the Forestry Commission into making more effort to establish the extent of the problem.[13]

Annual tree surveys produced by the Forestry Commission have subsequently shown a distinct trend for the worse in the status of trees. Its 1985 survey argued that there was "no scientific evidence nor any circumstantial evidence in Britain today which points to air pollution causing damage to trees other than locally".[14] By contrast, its 1986 survey concluded that the health of British conifers could only be considered "moderate". Appreciably more trees were "slightly" or "moderately" damaged than was the case in West Germany; the number of trees that were "slightly" damaged had doubled between 1985 and 1986, the number of trees with medium damage had quadrupled, and almost all the Norway spruce over the age of sixty that were examined were damaged.[15]

In 1987, new and shocking revelations came in a 15-country survey by the UN's Co-operative Programme for the Monitoring and Evaluation of Long-Range Transmission of Air Pollutants in Europe. The survey revealed that 67% of the United Kingdom's conifers were suffering slight to severe damage, and 28.9% had moderate to severe damage.[16]

Claims by MAFF that there was no evidence of discernible damage to UK agriculture in general were dismissed in 1984 by the House of Commons Environment Committee (see below) as "complacent and founded upon little other than conjecture".[17] Measurements undertaken by Harwell Laboratory in Oxfordshire in

1983 revealed that ozone concentrations rose above levels thought to cause crop damage on twenty-four days.[18] A 1983 EC-sponsored study by Imperial College London into the effects of SO_2 and NO_x on the black bean aphid – an important crop pest – found that in addition to any direct damage being done to crops by pollutants, chemical changes induced in plants enhanced the growth of insects feeding on them.[19] More recently, reports from Belgium and the Netherlands of damage to trees and vegetation near factory farms has led to research into the effects of ammonia given off by animal wastes. Traditional dung heaps on UK farms have been replaced on factory farms by open pools of animal waste in the form of liquid slurry. In the past thirty years, the quantity of ammonia fumes has grown by 55%; high concentrations of ammonia in the air may speed up the oxidation of SO_2.[20]

There is compelling evidence, too, of damage to buildings. Throughout the early 1980s, the CEGB dismissed any connection between emissions from its power stations and corrosion to buildings, arguing that it would take 5,000–20,000 years to dissolve an inch of limestone. In 1983 the CEGB suggested that it was "well established by international experts that the principal cause of stonework corrosion is high concentrations of gaseous pollutants. These. . .occur only in urban areas and are the result of many small sources of pollution with power stations making only a minor contribution".[21]

The 1984 Commons Committee dismissed this attitude as "trite and evasive", and listed some notable examples of damage to buildings:

○ In the period 1973–83, £5 million was spent on restoration of the stonework of Westminster Abbey. Much of the damage was ascribed to SO_2 and other gases. In 1894, forty-four flying buttresses on the south face of the abbey had been rebuilt in limestone; they now needed replacement because of SO_2 damage. In 1985 I was shown the work being undertaken on the abbey. When I asked the director of the restoration appeal what had caused all the damage, he unhesitatingly replied "acid rain".

○ The fact that stones of the thirteenth, eighteenth and nineteenth

centuries on Beverly Minster (near Hull) had been indiscrimin-
ately affected by decay confirmed that damaging pollution was
relatively recent in the whole life of the building.

o The copper sheeting on the roof of Liverpool Cathedral probably
needed replacing. There was evidence of a link between acid rain
and the deterioration of the sheeting, which was at its worst at the
points where rainwater was longest retained.

The Senior Sculpture Conservator at London's Victoria and
Albert Museum, whose department had researched stone decay
for twenty years, told the Commons Committee that the problem
of decay had "accelerated dramatically" since the turn of the century;
that rural as well as urban areas were affected, and that no technology
existed to preserve any stone sculpture in an external environment.
There was no known method of reducing weathering caused by air
pollutants except to reduce the SO_2 levels themselves, he noted.[22]
Evidence of the decay of the stonework on St Paul's Cathedral is
immediately visible to anyone visiting the observation level outside
the dome. An average of over 30 mm of Portland stone has been
lost in the past 250 years; in one particularly exposed position, 22
mm has been lost in just forty-five years.[23]

Despite all this evidence, the Building Effects Review Group
(BERG) – a UK government committee set up in 1985 to review
the effect of acid rain on buildings – reported in the summer of
1988 that there was insufficient evidence to make the link, although
it argued that it had not yet reviewed enough evidence to reach an
adequate judgement. The group was studying twenty-nine sites in
the United Kingdom and forty sites in Western Europe and North
America.[24]

The 1984 Commons and Lords reports

In its 1984 annual report, the Royal Commission on Environmental
Pollution described UK pollution control policy as suffering from
inadequate resources, secretiveness, isolationism and a lack of forward planning and continuity, and of failing to keep abreast of
pressing environmental problems.[25] Two further reports published
during 1984 subjected the policy to even closer scrutiny.

The first report[26] – by the Environment Committee of the House of Commons – was the most comprehensive. The Committee emphasized that it had begun its inquiry with an open mind, yet it was now convinced that "immediate and hard financial decisions have to be taken as time is running out. Simply to plead for more research into cause and effect is but to procrastinate. Enough is now known to justify the development and application of technology for removing the causes and effects now abundantly apparent." The study noted that despite the 37% drop in UK emissions since 1970, the United Kingdom was still (and in 1989 remains) the largest producer of SO_2 in Western Europe.

The second report[27] – by the House of Lords European Communities Committee – was published in June 1984 and examined the implications of EC policy on the United Kingdom. It was more hesitant than the Commons report, criticizing the scientific assessments made by the European Commission as the basis for five proposed new pieces of legislation, challenging the Commission's assumption that there was a linear relationship between emissions and deposition, and arguing that the evidence of a link between acid deposition and damage to trees was not as clear as the Commission suggested. The evidence available did not justify the expenditure and "environmental damage" that would result from using flue gas desulphurization (FGD) to achieve the 60% reduction in SO_2 emissions proposed by the Commission. The Committee favoured the use of pressurized fluidized bed combustion (PFBC), although it was "not appropriate" that emissions from coal-fired power stations should continue unabated until PFBC technology was ready in the 1990s.

On the other hand, the Committee acknowledged that acid pollution was a serious threat, and that it would be "foolish and dangerous" not to take action to combat the problem. "The magnitude of the damage resulting, the length of time over which this might become apparent, and its widespread effects if the fears expressed prove to be justified, make it necessary to implement a preventive programme now, despite the scientific uncertainties." The Committee recommended that at least two of the United Kingdom's power stations should immediately be fitted with FGD equipment. The Lords Committee also recommended that the United Kingdom should aim at reducing SO_2 emissions by at least 30%.

Summing up its findings, the Commons Committee emphasized that its inquiry had left it "deeply disturbed" over the United Kingdom's policy position on acid rain. It believed that sufficient evidence existed to show that an immediate decision to reduce emissions of SO_2, NO_x and hydrocarbons (HC) was needed. The Commons committee recommended that:

o   the United Kingdom immediately join the 30% Club;
o   the 30% cut in emissions be achieved by requiring the CEGB to reduce its emissions accordingly;
o   in the medium-term, as power stations came to be refitted, the CEGB should be required to install the equipment necessary to achieve a 60% national reduction in emissions by 1995, in line with the 1984 EC draft directive (see chapter 6);
o   the quickest way to reduce emissions was through retrofitting power stations;
o   to help reduce NO_x emissions, all power stations should install low NO_x burners; all industries other than those dependent on high combustion temperatures install low NO_x burners in existing plants; new motor vehicles be required to have reduced NO_x emission levels by 40% by the beginning of 1987; and the Department of Transport investigate the best possible means of reducing emissions from existing motor vehicles.

The Thatcher administration rejected the joint recommendation from the Houses of Commons and Lords to cut SO_2 emissions, refused to support the EC directive on SO_2 and NO_x emissions, turned down a proposal for a £1.4 billion project to reduce emissions from twelve UK power stations and refused to join the 30% Club. The only recommendation accepted from the Commons Committee report was the need for further monitoring and research. The Committee chairperson, Conservative Sir Hugh Rossi, called the government's refusal to join the 30% Club "inexplicable" and said the United Kingdom's acid rain policy displayed a "regrettable lack of good neighbourliness."

Lord Marshall, Margaret Thatcher and the Scandinavians

UK acid rain policy in the early 1980s was determined in large part by the CEGB and – to a lesser extent – the National Coal Board (NCB). The CEGB is the United Kingdom's largest electricity producer (accounting for 80–90% of its electricity), the NCB's largest customer, and cause of about 60% of the country's total SO_2 emissions. It controls seventy-eight power stations, forty of which are coal-fired, ten nuclear, and the rest powered by oil, gas or hydro-power.[28]

Both the NCB and the CEGB were consistently unwilling during this time to acknowledge any link between fossil fuels and acid pollution. In 1984, Sir Ian MacGregor (chairperson of the NCB from 1983 to 1986) claimed that the United Kingdom made only a small contribution to SO_2 emissions (less than 7% of the total for Europe, including the Soviet Union), and that it had reduced the amount by more than 30% over the last twelve years. The United Kingdom's SO_2 emissions indeed fell by 37% between 1970 and 1984, but not through pollution control. They fell because of production cutbacks in the wake of industrial recession, and the increasing use of sulphur-free natural gas (which now supplies more than 20% of the country's primary energy).

MacGregor further argued that remedial action forced upon energy producers could be so expensive that energy costs would rise, reducing their competitiveness and affecting jobs. He added:

> There is a distinct possibility that after we have crippled some of our basic industries we could then find we had not solved the [acid rain] problem. If all industrial activity ceased tomorrow there would still be acid rain for natural reasons and there always will be. . .It would be folly to adopt enormously expensive counter-measures which might in twenty years prove to have been unsuccessful.

The CEGB for its part regularly pointed with some satisfaction to the success of its post-war policy of building tall smokestacks in dispersing emissions. This is known to have contributed, for instance, to the reduction of London's once notorious smogs, but

– as the CEGB failed to observe – simply distributed the pollution further afield. The 1984 Commons report argued that there had been no significant reduction in CEGB emissions during the period 1972–1982, when total UK emissions fell (CEGB emission reductions accounted for only 14% of total UK reductions): "If action is to be taken to control the volume of UK emissions," the report concluded, "it could therefore be focused largely on this single source".

Ironically, the miners' strike of 1984–85 had the unexpected effect of increasing SO_2 emissions from the United Kingdom by an estimated 8,000 tonnes per month. Power stations normally fired by coal switched largely to oil, which has a higher sulphur content than domestic coal. Scientists at the University of Sussex estimated that UK SO_2 emissions from power stations in August 1984 were 18% higher than those of the previous August.[29]

Throughout the 1970s and early 1980s, the CEGB consistently refused to acknowledge the possibility that it was responsible for much of the acid pollution in Scandinavia. It argued that life was dying in Scandinavian lakes at the turn of the century, well before tall stacks were built. The cheapest way to reduce the acidity of those lakes, the CEGB argued, was to dose them with limestone. This would have the added benefit of giving scientists more time to establish the facts behind acidification.

Perhaps the pivotal figure in the debate has been one man: Lord Marshall of Goring, chairperson of the CEGB since 1982. Marshall long argued that the links between UK power stations and Scandinavian acid pollution had not been proven, and that until they were, any spending on emission control would be wasted money. In 1983, he argued that a threefold reduction in SO_2 emissions from the United Kingdom would probably cost more than £4 billion, with a continuous ongoing annual cost equivalent to £700 million: "If we consider the whole of Western Europe," he argued, "these figures rise by at least a factor of five. Since electricity is essential to everyone, this will effectively lower everyone's standard of living and it would be tragic to do this without understanding exactly what we are accomplishing".

The CEGB responded to the 1984 Lords report by arguing that the scientific evidence was either dubious or missing, and that the measures suggested would cost £2 billion, raise electricity costs by 10%, and increase unemployment. In an editorial comment, the *Guardian* suggested thhat the CEGB was using scare tactics, and that the cost (if spread over nine years) was well within the electricity budget.[30] Lord Marshall repeated the CEGB view that cutting sulphur emissions was too expensive and of no proven benefit to the environment. However, he said, acidifying emissions from CEGB power plants would be decreased, and the Board planned to experiment with the reduction of NO_x emissions from some plants by using two-step combustion: first burning the coal in chambers with little oxygen supply, and then changing the air streams in the boiler to reduce the formation of NO_x. Some CEGB boilers can easily be rebuilt for the purpose, but the Board claimed that it would cost close to £90 million to have all the boilers changed.

The CEGB had also begun showing some interest in obtaining more effective combustion in fluidized beds. Announcing the launch in October 1984 of four research projects aimed at removing SO_2 and NO_x from coal-fired power station emissions, Lord Marshall argued that acid rain was "a woolly definition covering a range of pollutants that require very different control measures":

> The research we have been doing over the last four years leads us to suspect that cuts in hydrocarbons from vehicles and other oil-burning appliances, and nitrogen oxides, may actually be more important than sulphur dioxide reductions, both for forests and for acid rain. . .If reductions [in NO_x] would be environmentally cost effective, we would certainly want to be in a position to act, just as we are on sulphur dioxide.[31]

In January 1985 the CEGB and NCB began a joint two-year £25 million project to develop an experimental PFBC furnace (the largest in the world) at Grimethorpe in South Yorkshire. In January 1988, the CEGB announced that PFBC would not be economical for anything other than small power stations, and that it was pinning its hopes instead on the coal gasification combined cycle technology (see chapter 3).[32]

The most vociferous critics of the UK policy position on acid rain have been the Scandinavians, particularly the Swedes and the Norwegians. According to the Norwegian Meteorological Institute, the United Kingdom is responsible for 10% of Norway's acid pollution as a whole, although the proportion rises to 16% in the most heavily polluted southern region of the country.[33] In 1983, a £5 million five-year study was launched by the Royal Society, the Norwegian Academy of Sciences and the Royal Swedish Academy of Sciences, with financing from the NCB and the CEGB. The object of the Surface Water Acidification Project (SWAP) was to study the impact of acid rain on the soil, waterways and fisheries of Norway and Sweden.

The study was greeted with anger by Scandinavian scientists, who argued that much of the research had already been done, and that the UK government was simply buying time. A year into the programme, only 2% of the budget had been spent and UK and Scandinavian scientists alike were complaining of bias in the way the money was being allocated. There was no procedure by which scientists could apply for grants; instead the committee administering the project itself decided which issues it wanted to investigate.

In 1985, Thatcher angered Norway's then-Prime Minister Kaar Willock by saying that the United Kingdom would do nothing to reduce SO_2 pollution from its power stations until the SWAP programme had reported. In March 1986, Norway's Environment Minister Rakel Surlien managed to elicit some sympathy from William Waldegrave, who said that the United Kingdom would be reviewing its acid pollution policy, and agreed that Norway's campaign had been "a model of how to persuade a friendly neighbour".[34] By 1986, the UK scientists on the project were being accused by their Norwegian counterparts of trying to stifle the first results. The five Britons apparently used their majority to reverse a previous decision to publish annual reports on the progress of the project. Quarterly meetings were abandoned, the project fell a year behind schedule, and there is now little chance of official results being published until 1990.[35]

Despite the hesitancy and inconsistency of its public statements, the Thatcher administration did not always take criticism of its acid pollution policy lightly. Apparently concerned at the United Kingdom's isolation following the West German turnabout in 1982, Giles Shaw, then parliamentary undersecretary in the Department of the Environment, ordered a review of acid rain policy in order to find out what could be done – and how much it would cost – to cut SO_2 emissions over ten years.[36] Scientists in the Department of the Environment concluded that significant reductions could best be achieved by fitting FGD equipment in several existing large power stations. The CEGB apparently opposed the plan, and no support was received from other government departments, so the Treasury was able to veto the plan.

In May 1984, Thatcher called a briefing session on government acid pollution policy, involving senior scientists and ministers. She had probably been partly motivated by her campaign to win allies in the EC in support of the United Kingdom's attempts to reduce its budget contributions. According to the environmental monthly *ENDS Report*, William Waldegrave and Martin Holdgate (then respectively environment minister and chief scientist at the Department of the Environment), argued that the United Kingdom should signal willingness to join the 30% Club and take a positive line on NO_x reduction. But objections from the Treasury, Lord Marshall and Energy Minister Peter Walker persuaded the prime minister to defer any specific commitments.

At the 1984 Multilateral Conference on the Environment in Munich, Waldegrave argued that, while the United Kingdom had "difficulty" with an immediate commitment to join the 30% Club, it was prepared to promise making "further substantial" SO_2 reductions (in addition to the 20% reduction since 1980) in a "reasonable time-scale", and "parallel" cuts in NO_x. Holdgate told the conference that the United Kingdom wished to see the environmental deterioration caused by air pollution halted and, where possible, reversed, but that government concern was "to base action on a proper understanding of the factors that change and damage the environment." At the July 1985 meeting of the Executive Board of the Economic Commission for Europe (ECE) convention in Helsinki, Waldegrave said that the United Kingdom counted itself among the countries committed to reducing SO_2 and NO_x emissions; it had reduced SO_2 emissions by 42% since 1970, and by 25% since 1980, by using low-sulphur fuels, using energy more efficiently, and by "industrial restructuring" (a phrase interpreted by government critics as "industrial recession"). Further reductions of SO_2 and NO_x were planned, aimed at a reduction on 1980 levels of 30%

by the end of the 1990s. (Waldegrave hinted that expanded nuclear energy capacity would be one factor in the continued reductions.)

Thatcher also faced criticism from members of her own party. The Bow Group, supported by ninety-five centre-left Conservative members of parliament, argued in mid-1984 that the Conservative Party would "reap electoral credit" if the government were to agree to cut SO_2 and NO_x emissions, and that the United Kingdom should join the 30% Club.[37] In December 1984, Conservative members of the European Parliament decided not only to join the majority group of MEPs critical of the UK government position, but also to put themselves at the head of this group. They believed that they had the tacit support of Environment Secretary Patrick Jenkin, of Foreign Secretary Sir Geoffrey Howe, and of Waldegrave, and that their open opposition could encourage the Council of Ministers to override a UK veto of the EC directive on large plant emissions.

As scientific research progressed and the acid rain lobby became more vocal in the mid-1980s, Thatcher, Lord Marshall and the CEGB became increasingly embattled and isolated. Criticism of the CEGB came not only from the Scandinavians, but also from the select Committees of the Commons and the Lords, government agencies such as the Nature Conservancy Council, private interest groups and from the Department of the Environment itself, which was privately very critical of the Board's attitude.[38] The CEGB attitude was exemplified in 1986, when it caused much dismay by producing a £300,000 video called "Acid Rain" in which it implied that Norwegian scientists were wrong to attribute declines in their fisheries to acid pollution, and pointed instead to changes in land use as the source of the problem. Based almost entirely on interviews with individuals paid directly or indirectly by the CEGB, the video by implication questioned the credibility of scientists working on the problem, hinting that decisions were being made on emotional rather than scientific grounds.[39]

Only months later, in September 1986, Lord Marshall finally admitted that the CEGB was at least partly to blame for the United Kingdom's acid emissions, and offered to spend £600 million by 1996 to cut them (by controlling emissions from three coal-fired power stations). The United Kingdom's worsening relations with Norway proved a key incentive, along with the growing weight of scientific evidence. Two particular pieces of evidence seemed to have made the difference: a Swedish study repeating an extensive study of the acidity of forest soils in 1927, which found that the acidity of soils at a depth of 70 cm (28 inches) was almost uniformly ten times greater than in 1927; and the discovery of the importance of sulphate ions (in addition to hydrogen ions) in leaching cations into streams and lakes, making them acid.[40]

Lord Marshall's conversion was not yet absolute, however. While accepting that as much as a quarter of the cumulative total of acid rain that had fallen on Norway in the past 125 years came from the United Kingdom, he argued that even if all emissions ceased immediately, acid and sulphur would continue to flow out of Scandinavian soils for many years to come. Hence he believed that there was no great urgency in reducing emissions, but that a steady, continued reduction would allow stored acidity to be washed out of the soils.[41] (Despite Lord Marshall's new position, the CEGB continued to work on the theory that 30–50% of the total sulphur acids in Scandinavian air in the summer could be generated by North Sea plankton.)[42]

The final step in the United Kingdom's conversion came in June 1988, when the Thatcher administration finally agreed to the terms of the EC directive, committing itself to reducing SO_2 emissions by 60% by the year 2003, and NO_x emissions by 30% by 1998. To do this, the CEGB believes it will have to fit FGD to power plants with a total capacity of 12,000 megawatts, at a cost of £1.2 billion. But this estimate may be optimistic. Philip Comer, a Department of the Environment consultant, argued in a 1988 report for the DoE that plants with a capacity of 29,000 MW would need to be converted, at a total cost of £3 billion. Comer believed that the building of new nuclear power plants and coal-fired plants fitted with FGD, together with the closure of old power stations, would reduce emissions by 14%; the rest of the reductions would have to come from retrofitting FGD equipment to existing plants.[43]

Acid rain and the policy process

During the critical period since the late 1970s, when pressure has grown on governments to curb acid pollution, the United Kingdom has been governed by an administration actively opposed to the imposition of controls on industry. In her plans for the country's economic revival, Thatcher has generally rejected attempts to impose regulation, preferring instead that industry be free to respond to market demands. But natural resources like the air are part of the global commons. The argument of Thatcherism – that regulation can be imposed by the market – does not necessarily apply to resources in the public sphere. Environmental control demands public regulation, a notion to which the Thatcher government has been loathe to accede. In the face of increasingly compelling evidence of the link between emissions and pollution, government justifications for its acid pollution policy in the mid-1980s began to sound increasingly contrived and indefensible to its critics.

Why did United Kingdom not sign the ECE convention on SO_2? Speaking in 1985 at the Helsinki meeting of the ECE convention executive board, Environment Minister Waldegrave said it was because the United Kingdom could not be "absolutely certain about the likely change in [its] sulphur dioxide emissions over the next decade", and because it was not absolutely certain that it could meet the target of a 30% reduction by 1993. "It may well be," he said, "that even though we are not able to sign [the SO_2 protocol], our actual performance will be equal to or better than that of a number of countries that do." (This rather supercilious attitude has since been largely discredited. All the ECE signatories except those in Eastern Europe have not only met the terms of the convention, but in some cases have exceeded it (see table 4.2, chapter 4). The United Kingdom also regarded the terms of the SO_2 protocol as "arbitrary": while emissions from some other countries had risen during the 1970s, Waldegrave argued, the United Kingdom had made a "significant contribution" to SO_2 reductions in Europe; if the terms of the protocol had been a 40% reduction on the year of peak emissions, the United Kingdom would already have met that condition.

By agreeing to the EC Directive in 1988, though, the United Kingdom went well beyond the terms of the ECE convention, even if the time frame was longer. Why then did it take so long to change its position? There are several possible explanations. First, pressure on the government took the form largely of public criticism and polite diplomatic negotiation, and came as much from non-governmental organizations (NGOs) as from other governments. NGOs play a very large part in determining and carrying out UK environmental policy, but Thatcher has long regarded most of them as subversive, and so has paid little heed to their demands. For all the protests from other European governments (such as the February 1984 Nordic environment ministers joint statement encouraging the United Kingdom to rethink its position and agree to join the 30% Club), there was little direct pressure exerted on government.

Second, although many Britons are now aware in general terms of the acid pollution problem, it has never been the major public issue that it became in West Germany and Scandinavia. The countryside has long been the key environmental issue in the United Kingdom, and agricultural intensification is seen as the main threat to the countryside; hence the efforts of many UK environmental organizations are focused on this. The countryside plays roughly the same role in the UK national psyche as forests play in West Germany, or wilderness in the United States. It was only when damage to German forests was clearly and widely visible that the West German government agreed to action. As acid damage to the UK countryside became more visible, public pressure increased.

Third, the environmental policy-making structure in the United Kingdom (as in many other countries) is confused and piecemeal. The misnamed Department of the Environment is more interested in local government issues than in the natural environment. There have been repeated suggestions for a restructuring of the department, with its environmental protection components being set up in a new, separate department. (The low priority given by the department to environmental affairs was exemplified during the late 1980s by the notable lack of interest shown in the environment by the Secretary of State, Nicholas Ridley.)

Without any rational or logical decision-making structure, organizations like the CEGB have a remarkable degree of freedom of action. Without a clear policy-making structure, policy is determined as much as anything by the governed rather than the governors.

As long as the CEGB was unconvinced of the national economic benefits of reducing emissions, there was little likelihood of any substantive reductions in UK emissions. Ironically, the country that stands to benefit most from a reduction in UK emissions is the United Kingdom itself, which generates nearly 90% of its own depositions.

Fourth, although the United Kingdom contributes to acid pollution damage elsewhere in Europe, it receives very few emissions from outside its own borders. A 1984 Warren Spring report suggested that other countries accounted for as little as 11% of all acidity in UK rainfall. There is a direct relationship in most cases between the proportion of received pollution and the environmental activism of the government of a given country. A critical element in Canadian, Scandinavian and West German policy calculations has been the fact that much of the pollution (45–65%) in these countries is received. In order to deal with such pollution, domestic action has been particularly urgent in terms of setting an example. The United Kingdom has been under no such compulsion.

Fifth, the UK government consistently argued that not enough was known about the causes of acid pollution, and that action was inadvisable until the link was firmly established. The preoccupation, noted Holdgate, was "to try to approach the subject in an honest, dispassionate, factual way".[44] But this was always likely to be seen as "obdurate self interest rather than commendable caution", argued the United Kingdom's Earth Resources Research group.[45] The need for scientific certainty was an argument used with similar frequency by the Reagan administration. Many of the critics of UK and American policies argued that this was simply a smoke-screen, but there were others in the United Kingdom who were genuinely surprised that the logic of UK policy was not abundantly clear.

The Thatcher administration consistently argued that the quantity and quality of evidence of acid pollution damage in the United Kingdom was too variable. Monitoring undertaken in urban centres had revealed a fall in winter concentrations of SO_2 since the 1960s, which has only to be expected in the wake of the construction of taller smoke stacks. But, as the 1984 Commons

Committee emphasized, there has been a noticeable lack of rural monitoring programmes, and no data has been available to show if rural levels of pollution have increased since the introduction of tall stacks. The Warren Spring report showed that many parts of the rural United Kingdom were not monitored for SO_2, NO_x rainfall pH or ozone. Warren Spring itself ran only three NO_x monitoring stations. In response to the Warren Spring report, the Department of the Environment in 1984 announced that twenty-five new acid deposition monitoring stations were to be established and £750,000 spent on improving existing stations. Such research programmes as do exist are frequently used as an excuse for inaction. In 1983 a Department of the Environment spokesperson told *New Scientist* that "as far as we're concerned research is action".

Finally, UK policy-makers often argue that the United Kingdom takes its commitments to international agreements very seriously, and strives to live up to its obligations. The UK government argued for some time that it would be wrong be commit itself to a 30% reduction in SO_2 emissions by 1993 unless it was absolutely certain that it could meet that target. This all sounds very commendable, but against the background of Prime Minister Thatcher's determination not to impose additional burdens and limits on industry, it is difficult to accept it as a legitimate policy argument.

Even so, despite everything that had gone before, events in United Kingdom at the end of 1988 and the beginning of 1989 put an entirely new complexion on UK environmental policy. After nine years of stubborn resistance to the environmental movement, Thatcher suddenly and remarkably became an environmentalist, or so it seemed – the rapidity of her conversion led many sceptics to doubt her sincerity. The change began with her September 1988 Royal Society speech. Five months later, environmentalists were still reeling at the sight of Thatcher taking the spotlight at the London conference on the ozone layer, arguing that policy makers and governments had to come together to solve global environmental problems. In the 1989 budget, Chancellor Nigel Lawson took a tangible step by reducing the tax on unleaded petrol in an attempt to encourage UK motorists to convert from leaded fuel. It may have been a small step, but it seemed to confirm that things would never be quite the same again.

NOTES

1. *The Sunday Times*, 2 October 1988.
2. Pearce, Fred, "Acid rain: new fears prompted clean up", in *New Scientist*, 18 September 1986, pp. 22–3.
3. As quoted in Don Hinrichsen, "Acid rain and forest decline" in Edward Goldsmith and Nicholas Hildyard (eds), *The Earth Report: The Essential Guide to Global Ecological Issues* (Los Angeles: Price Stern Sloan Inc., 1988).
4. UN Economic Commission for Europe, *National Strategies and Policies for Air Pollution Abatement* (New York: United Nations, 1987).
5. UK Review Group on Acid Rain, *Acid Deposition in the United Kingdom*, (Warren Spring Laboratory, Stevenage, Herts, 1984).
6. Cowling, Ellis, "Acid precipitation in historical perspective", in *Environmental Science and Technology* 16:2, (January 1982). pp. 110A–22A.
7. Henriksen, Arne and Hans Seip, *Strong and weak acids in surface waters of southern Norway and southwestern Scotland*, SNSF Project Report, FR 17/80, (1980).
8. "Acid secrets beneath the lochs of Galloway", *New Scientist*, 23 January 1986, p. 35.
9. Howells, W.R., *The effects of acid precipitation and land use on water quality and ecology in Wales and the implications for the Authority*, Report for Welsh Water Authority, (Powys: 27 April 1983).
10. Lines, Roger, "Species and seed origin trials in the industrial Pennines", in *Quarterly Journal of Forestry*, 28:1, 1984, pp. 9–23.
11. House of Commons Environment Committee, *Fourth Report: Acid Rain* (London: HMSO, 1984).
12. Elsworth, Steve, "A 'moderate' cause for alarm", in *New Scientist*, 12 February 1987, p. 66.
13. Pearce, Fred, *Acid Rain* (Harmondsworth: Penguin, 1987).
14. Elsworth, see note 12.
15. Forestry Commission, *Forest Health and Air Pollution, 1986 Survey* (London: HMSO, 1986).
16. UNECE, see note 4.
17. House of Commons Environment Committee, see note 11.
18. AERE–R11382, *Ambient ozone measurements at Harwell, Jan–Dec 1983* (London: HMSO, 1984).
19. Dohmen, G.P., S. McNeill, and J.N.B. Bell, "Air pollution increases

Aphis fabae pest potential", in *Nature* 307:5946, 5–11 January 1984, pp. 52–3.

20. Pearce, Fred, "Are cows killing Britains's trees?", in *New Scientist*, 23 October 1986, p. 20.

21. *New Scientist*, 13 September 1983.

22. House of Commons Environment Committee, see note 11.

23. Dudley, Nigel, Mark Barrett and David Baldock, *The Acid Rain Controversy* (London: Earth Resources Research, 1985).

24. *New Scientist*, 2 June 1988.

25. RCEP *Annual Report 1984* (London: HMSO).

26. House of Commons Environment Committee, see note 11.

27. House of Lords Select Committee on the European Communities, *22nd Report: Air Pollution* (London: HMSO, 1984).

28. Fells, Ian, "The trials of privatising electricity", in *New Scientist*, 11 February 1988, pp. 38–40.

29. *New Scientist*, 27 November 1984.

30. The *Guardian*, 12 August 1984.

31. *The Times*, 10 October 1984.

32. "CEGB dumps fluidised bed", in *New Scientist*, 4 February 1988, p. 27.

33. "Britain and US accept the science of acid rain", in *New Scientist*, 27 March 1986, p. 11.

34. *New Scientist*, see note 33.

35. "Norwegians protest over gag on research", *New Scientist*, 20 March 1986, p. 24.

36. *New Scientist*, 15 September 1984.

37. *A role for Britain in the acid rainstorm* (London: Bow Publications, 1984).

38. Fry, Garry, Ivar Muniz and Arnie Semb, "Nice video, shame about the fish", in *New Scientist*, 27 March 1986, pp. 46–7.

39. Fry, Garry, and others, see note 38.

40. Pearce, Fred, "Unravelling a century of acid pollution", in *New Scientist*, 25 September 1986, pp. 23–4.

41. Pearce, Fred, see note 40.

42. Pearce, Fred, "Plankton share the blame for sulphur pollution", in *New Scientist*, 11 February 1988, p. 25.

43. Pearce, Fred, "Cost of acid cleanup doubles", in *New Scientist*, 22 October 1988, p. 29.

44. House of Commons Environment Committee, see note 11.

45. Dudley and others, see note 23.

6. Western Europe – the Community Approach

The nineteen nations of Western Europe are mostly small, close together, and industrialized. This makes them prone to trans-boundary pollution problems. The United Kingdom was probably the first seriously polluted country in Western Europe, and the first to respond with pollution control agencies and anti-pollution laws. But even though it was a Scottish chemist who first identified acid pollution, it was the Scandinavians who first drew widespread international attention to the problem, mainly because of the pollution they were receiving from their neighbours. The Austrians, the Swiss and the French have since made the greatest strides in reducing SO_2 emissions, with cuts of about 50% in the period 1980–1986. And pollution has provided impetus to the creation of green parties in thirteen West European countries, eight of which returned members to their national parliaments between 1979 and 1988.[1]

Although the UN Economic Commission for Europe (ECE) has been active in attempts to reach international agreement on SO_2 and NO_x controls, the organization which has probably made the biggest and most effective strides in actually implementing SO_2 controls is the European Community (EC). With several different means at its disposal for imposing (or, at least, encouraging agreement on) binding controls on its member states, the EC has proved a vital influence on European environmental policy. Gregory Wetstone and Armin Rosencranz call the EC "the organization most likely to eventually succeed in establishing international SO_2 control programmes in response to Europe's transboundary pollution problem".[2] For Nigel Haigh, environmental policy "can now be counted as one of the quiet success stories of the Community".[3]

Even the United Kingdom, too often a reluctant European country, was finally committed in 1988 to SO_2 controls by an EC Directive – this after years of stalling, and of pressure brought to bear by its neighbours using channels other than the EC.

The EC: the organization most likely to succeed

The EC is the only international organization with the power to agree pollution control policies binding on its member states.[4] Its policy is outlined in four Programmes of Action, agreed in 1973, 1977, 1982 and 1987. The direct administration of environmental policies is left to member states themselves, but the EC has five legislative tools available to it: Regulations, Directives, Decisions, Recommendations and Opinions.[5] Of all these, the most important in terms of environmental policy are directives. Binding in terms of the ends to be achieved, but not the means, they are flexible enough to accommodate existing national procedures, which makes them useful for pollution control. Derogations to a directive can be made for individual countries unable to meet its terms. (For example, Ireland asked for a five-year extension on the 1981 deadline set by the 1978 directive on lead in petrol.)

At the June 1983 meeting of the Heads of State and Government of the European Community in Stuttgart, a call was made for "immediate action" by the EC on acid rain to avoid an "irreversible situation", and for EC measures aimed at "rapid significant progress" towards acid pollution control. The Commission of the EC responded to the Stuttgart meeting with a five-point plan building on existing directives and proposing new measures. The plan included a revival of a 1976 proposal for a directive on sulphur emissions from the burning of fuel oil and a comprehensive package of measures to control vehicle emissions. Since the beginning of 1984, there has been a relative flood of proposals for new EC legislation, among other things suggesting regulations and directives on combatting air pollution from industrial plants, establishing a scheme to provide EC forests with increased protection against acid rain, limiting emissions from large combustion plants, and setting air quality standards for NO_x.

Among the directives that have been agreed so far are those on the sulphur content of gas oil, or light fuel oil, (adopted 1975); lead in petrol (1978 and (1985); air quality standards for suspended particulates (smoke) and SO_2 (1980); lead (1982); nitrogen dioxide (1985); emission of pollutants from industrial plants (1984) and large combustion plants (1988), and several on vehicle exhaust emissions introduced since 1974. Two directives are particularly important: one on smoke and SO_2, and the other on pollutants from large combustion plants. The first sets limits on ground level concentrations of SO_2 and smoke, to be met at the latest by 1993. It was initially opposed by the United Kingdom (which objected to a Community-wide air quality standard), Ireland (which felt it would hamper its plans for industrial expansion) and West Germany (which felt the techniques for measurement were too imprecise). But the accession of all the EC member states to the ECE convention made the dissenters less inclined to oppose the SO_2 directive, and it was adopted in 1980.

The combustion plant directive (which has had so much impact on UK policy) limits total emissions from power plants over 50 MW and requires an SO_2 emission reduction of 58% on 1980 levels, to be achieved in three phases. The norm will be −23% by 1993, −42% by 1998 and −58% by 2003. The United Kingdom plans the following rates of reduction: −20% by 1993, −40% by 1998 and −60% by 2003 (see table 6.1). The directive also requires NO_x emissions to be reduced. The norm will be −30% by 1998 (see table 6.2).

Dealing with EC vehicle emissions

Vehicle emission controls have proved a controversial issue in the EC. NO_x has been a growing problem, and its biggest source in Europe is cars. The heavy use of road vehicles has ensured that there is as much nitrogen in the air over most of Europe as there is sulphur. Cars are also the major source of hydrocarbons (HC), which with NO_x are a major component in the formation of ozone.

One of the answers to controlling vehicle emissions is to fit vehicles with catalytic converters, which remove some of the pollutants from exhaust gases (see chapter 3). The problem is that catalytic

Table 6.1: Planned sulphur dioxide reductions in the EC (thousand tonnes/year, power plants only)

	Emissions 1980	Emission ceilings 1993	1998	2003	% red'n over 1980 1993	1998	2003
Belgium	530	318	212	159	−40	−60	−70
Denmark	323	213	141	106	−34	−56	−67
W. Germany	2 225	1 335	890	668	−40	−60	−70
Greece	303	320	320	320	+6	+6	+6
Spain	2 290	2 290	1 730	1 440	0	−24	−37
France	1 910	1 146	764	573	−40	−60	−70
Ireland	99	124	124	124	+25	+25	+25
Italy	2 450	1 800	1 500	900	−27	−39	−63
Luxembourg	3	1.8	1.5	1.5	−40	−50	−60
Netherlands	299	180	120	90	−40	−60	−70
Portugal	115	232	270	206	+102	+135	+79
UK	3 883	3 106	2 330	1 553	−20	−40	−60
EC	**14 430**	**11 065**	**8 402**	**6 140**	**−23**	**−42**	**−58**

Source: ENDS Report 167, December 1988.

Table 6.2: Planned nitrogen oxide reduction in the EC (thousand tonnes/year, power plants only)

	Emissions 1980	Emission ceilings 1993	1998	% red'n over 1980 1993	1998
Belgium	110	88	66	−20	−40
Denmark	124	121	81	−3	−35
W. Germany	870	696	522	−20	−40
Greece	36	70	70	+94	+94
Spain	366	368	277	+1	−24
France	400	320	240	−20	−40
Ireland	28	50	50	+79	+79
Italy	580	570	428	−2	−26
Luxembourg	3	2.4	1.8	−20	−40
Netherlands	122	98	73	−20	−40
Portugal	23	59	64	+157	+178
UK	1 016	864	711	−15	−30
EC	**3 678**	**3 306**	**2 538**	**−10**	**−30**

Source: ENDS Report 167, December 1988.

converters do not work well with leaded fuel, hence the need to reduce the amount of lead in petrol. Lead in petrol has also been an important health issue (it can lead to anaemia and neurological disorders, particularly in children). Lead is added to petrol to improve its performance in high compression engines. Reduction of lead levels became an EC policy issue as long ago as 1971, when West Germany first proposed legislation restricting its use.

After much debate, the EC agreed on its 1978 directive, allowing member states to set limits at between 0.15–0.40 g/l. (0.15 g/l is near the lowest level usable in existing vehicle engines without special modifications – the minimum limit was set to ensure that no barriers to trade in motor vehicles could be created by a member state insisting on unleaded petrol.)

The EC proposed a two-stage conversion to unleaded fuel: by 1989 for new model vehicles and by 1991 for all new vehicles, followed in 1995 by the application of US emission standards. But in 1983, West Germany pre-empted everyone by announcing that unleaded petrol and catalytic converters for all new vehicles would be mandatory from 1 January 1986.

The EC charged that the West German move was illegal under existing directives, which bar member states from banning imports of any vehicles that meet EC standards. West German car manufacturers protested that their government's ban against vehicles without converters would draw retaliation from other EC countries, and UK car manufacturers argued that catalytic converters would increase petrol consumption by 10%. France, Italy and the United Kingdom argued that the West German move would break up the EC road vehicle market and lead to a flood of Japanese cars already fitted with emission controls. France formally complained to the European Commission that West German plans amounted to a barrier to trade under the Treaty of Rome. West Germany for its part quoted Article 36 of the Treaty of Rome, which allows the imposition of trade restrictions on grounds that include "the protection of health and life of humans, animals or plants".

In January 1984 there were signs that the West Germans were beginning to doubt that they could meet their own deadline. In September 1984 they replaced the 1986 target with a decision that all cars sold there from 1 January 1989 would have to be fitted with catalytic converters, although voluntary controls would still be encouraged from July 1986, including providing motorists with incentives like cuts in car tax. This still anticipates by five years the timetable proposed by the EC. In December 1984 the Council of the EC adopted two directives: one agreeing that unleaded petrol must be on sale in all member states by 1 October 1989, and one setting limits on nitrogen dioxide in the air (agreed in March 1985). The European Commission also asked member states to try to agree Community-wide emission standards by the end of 1986.

The EC Council of Ministers agreed in June 1985 to establish standards on emissions from petrol-driven cars of carbon monoxide, HC with NO_x, and NO_x alone. The standards take into account European driving patterns, and there are different standards for large cars (more than 2 litres), medium cars (1.4–2.0 litres) and small cars (less than 1.4 litres), and different timetables for the introduction of controls. By October 1994, every new car sold in the EC will have to comply; larger cars will have to fit catalytic converters, and smaller cars will use lean-burn engines.

Acid pollution in the EC: a country-by-country report

In 1980, the twelve countries that now make up the EC produced 21.5 million tonnes of SO_2 among them; most have since agreed to cut their emissions substantially. Only in two of the least industrialized of the twelve – Ireland and Portugal – are emissions on the rise (see table 6.1). The EC has estimated that reducing SO_2 emissions by 55–65% between 1980 and 2000 in its members states will cost \$4.6–\$6.7 billion per year, and that NO_x reductions of 10% in the same period will cost \$100–\$400 million per year.[6]

Every member state both emits and receives acid pollution, but the contribution of foreign and domestic pollution varies enormously. In 1980, the United Kingdom, Italy, France, Spain and West Germany between them accounted for 85% of the Community's SO_2 emmissions. Ironically, the countries receiving the greatest proportion of total deposition from foreign sources are two of the smallest producers: Luxembourg (73%) and the Netherlands (71%), while those receiving the least include three of the biggest producers: United Kingdom (12%), Spain (18%) and Italy (22%).

Despite the effect of EC legislation, different member countries have responded very differently to the acid rain problem. This is partly a reflection of the level and extent of damage identified in each country, and partly of the relative importance and structure of environmental policy-making in each country. For example, the environmental movement has been active for well over a century in the United Kingdom, and there is a strong public movement today; but threats to the countryside are given more priority than acid rain. In West Germany, the rise of the Greens has had a major influence on changes in policy. In Italy, pollution has been almost totally ignored until the last two to three years. Ireland is producing more and more SO_2, but argues that almost none of it passes across its boundaries, so domestic SO_2 controls would have no benefit for its EC partners.

Belgium

Belgium reduced its sulphur emissions by more than 42% between 1980 and 1984,[7] so it had already met the terms of its membership of the 30% Club by the time it joined in June 1984. But the most recent estimates suggest that its emissions will increase by 16% by 1995,[8] leaving a net decrease between 1980 and 1995 of 32%. This is still within the terms of the 30% Club. More than half Belgium's sulphur deposition comes from other other countries, mainly France, the United Kingdom and West Germany.

Belgian national air pollution control legislation, dating back to 1968, consists mainly of measures aimed at traffic and domestic heating (which account for 16% of emissions), while setting no emissions limits for industry and power stations. In 1983, regulations on SO_2 and suspended particulates were introduced in line with the 1980 EC directive, but as the levels had already been met in much of Belgium, this amounted to little more than legitimization of the status quo.[9] Most of the reductions were achieved by a shift from oil and coal to nuclear power. Belgian utilities argue that retrofitting power stations with flue gas desulphurization (FGD) systems would be too expensive, and there are fears that they may be using the acid pollution issue as an excuse to expand the nuclear power programme.

Acid damage in Belgium has barely been investigated. According to selective studies, rain over north-eastern Belgium has had pH values as low as 3.8 to 4. In Antwerp, the mean value is pH 4. Belgian soils are generally rich in buffering agents, but some regions are not. Some moorland pools in the Campine Fens, although naturally slightly acid, now have pH values as low as 3.8. Fish have disappeared from the fens, and in Wallonia trees show signs of damage, but in neither case has a link yet been made with acid pollution. Along the border with West Germany, 70% of forest cover is reported to be damaged. This may help account for the fact that the Walloon Green Party, Ecolo, won 16% of the vote in the region during the 1984 European Parliament elections, well above its national average.

Denmark

Denmark sends nearly two-thirds of its sulphur emissions transboundary, mainly to Sweden and Norway. It is a member of the 30% Club and, to meet its commitments, has been reducing the sulphur content of heavy and light fuel oils. This reduces emissions from local heating plants, domestic heating units and diesel-powered vehicles, which together account for about half its sulphur emissions. The remaining half comes from power stations. Government proposals to control these emissions rely partly on FGD. Between 1980 and 1985, Denmark cut its SO_2 emissions by 25%, so it was well on the way to meeting the terms of the 30% Club. A government Commission on Acidification estimated in 1984 that the total cost of achieving a 30% emissions reduction would be about DKr 3–4 billion ($180–240 million) over nine years, and would add less than 0.001 of a cent to the price of a kilowatt-hour of electricity by 1995.[10]

France

Until 1984, France – like West Germany and the United Kingdom – opposed pollution controls. Then, like West Germany, it switched sides and joined the 30% Club. It even went as far as committing itself to a 50% reduction in SO_2 emissions by 1990, and by 1985, it had already reduced these by 48%. While this may seem laudable on the surface, reduced SO_2 emissions have come in large part through further investment in what the French government likes to call "clean energy" – that is, nuclear power.

France has one of the most active nuclear power programmes in the world. In 1983, nearly half its electricity was generated by nuclear power and only 23% by solid fuels; today, about 70% is provided by nuclear power and by the year 2000, the proportion is expected to be up to 79%.[11] (Compare this to the respective figures in 1983 for West Germany, 2%; Italy, 4%; the United Kingdom, 7%).

Increased reliance on nuclear energy has meant that the state-owned Eléctricité de France, which supplies nearly 90% of the country's electricity, was able to cut its SO_2 emissions by 55% from 1980 to 1983 at no additional cost.[12] France also introduced in 1985 a system of "para-fiscal charges on air pollution", levied on all combustion plants larger than 50 MW that were emitting more than 2,500 tonnes of SO_2 or NO_x annually. The proceeds (130 francs per tonne of SO_2) are then used to develop new desulphurization technology.[13]

French concern about acid pollution has been notably low-key, which Peter Brackley suggests is a reflection of traditional French interest in people in society rather than in people within the natural environment.[14] France has 13.6 million hectares (33.6 million acres) of forest, covering nearly a quarter of the land area and constituting about a third of all the forests in the EC. Two-thirds of the trees are deciduous and the rest evergreen. Links between tree death and industrial pollution have long been known, but have apparently been less worrying to most people than damage from natural phenomena, such as intense cold, or the forest fires which annually burn down 40,000 hectares (100,000 acres) of woodland.[15]

Despite this, a national programme of research into forest damage – Dépérissement des Forêts Attribué à la Pollution Atmosphérique (DEFORPA) – was launched in 1984, with partial funding from the EC. Dry deposition seems to be the main problem in France. Among the most seriously affected forests are those in the Vosges highlands in the north-east. Following reports of damage in 1983, the environment ministry launched a monitoring programme there, and 200 observation posts were established to assess rain, air and water quality and tree growth. National Forestry Office figures published in June 1984 revealed that 35,000 hectares (86,000 acres) were affected, of which 5,000 hectares (12,000 acres) were seriously affected. In October 1984 the environment ministry admitted that 10% of the Vosges forest was affected. Studies in the southern Vosges found that trees die off faster after several days of good weather, suggesting a link with ozone formation. By early 1985, one in every five conifers in the Vosges was reported to be dying.

Forests in Alsace are also affected. DEFORPA studies in 1984 found that 20% of the resinous trees and 4% of the deciduous trees in the 310,000 hectares (770,000 acres) of public forest were affected.[16] In the Donon massif, firs have been losing their needles. The worst affected trees are those on higher ground and those exposed to southerly and south-westerly winds. Trees of all ages are damaged, including young saplings. Pine tops have been thinning, and since the autumn of 1983, even established trees of 3–4 m (10–13 ft) have been attacked by insects. Leaves on beeches have been found to be thinning and yellowing.[17] Other affected areas include Jura, the Alps, the Massif Central and the Pyrénées. One German scientist has claimed that there is an almost unbroken line of forest damage from Bretagne in the west to the Vosges in the east, but so far this has not been supported or recognized by the French.

If forest destruction is not as important to the French as it is to the West Germans, France may find it more difficult to ignore accelerating acid damage to its cultural heritage. A case in point is Rheims Cathedral. Renowned for the beauty of its sculpted exterior, the cathedral largely withstood the ravages of two world wars. But acid pollution is causing extensive flaking and crumbling stonework. Many of the 2,600 sculptures that adorn the exterior have lost their features. *Le Monde* reported in December 1988 that sculptures taken down for restoration looked like "mummies ready for burial".[18] Up to £14 million may have to be spent on Rheims in the next ten years. Elsewhere in France, damage has become so severe that buildings are threatened with collapse. *Le Monde* noted that the upper sections of the pinnacles of the buttresses on Beauvais Cathedral are now so weak that they sway in strong winds, and flying buttresses on Orléans and Tours Cathedrals are in danger of collapse.

Greece

Geographical separation from its EC partners means that Greece contributes little to their acid pollution; nearly two-thirds of its annual SO_2 emissions of 700,000 tonnes are redeposited within Greece. But more than half of the total deposition in Greece comes from foreign sources, including Italy. As a relatively lightly industrialized country, Greece's immediate problems come from smog, for which Athens is particularly notorious. Concern for the state of historic buildings and monuments in the capital as long ago as 1975 led to the formation of the Acropolis Committee, a group of architects, chemists and archaeologists pledged to restoring the Acropolis by 1991 at an estimated cost of $65 million. (One of the arguments used by those opposed to the return of the Elgin marbles is that their sojourn in the British Museum has protected them from damaging pollution.) In 1982, the government announced that a priority area for action was Attica. Strict emission controls had already been imposed there, including the exclusion of cars from the centre of Athens and the relocation away from it of heavy-polluting industries.[19]

SO_2 is less of a problem in Athens than NO_x from road traffic. Attempts have been made to reduce the number of cars in the city from the present figure of half a million. In January 1984, air pollution became so bad that the government ordered a 30% cut in industrial production, reduced central heating in public buildings, and banned some vehicles from the city. As the smog persisted, a 9,000–hectare (20,000–acre) zone was declared in which cars and taxis were allowed to travel only on alternate days.[20] In July 1984, a heat wave caused levels of smog in the city to rise so alarmingly that the government had to impose emergency measures to protect the health of Athenians and maintain its own political credibility. Half the private cars on the streets were ordered off for forty-eight hours and industries were told to cut fuel consumption by 30%. In the space of two days, about 500 people were hospitalized with respiratory complaints.[21]

Greece did not sign the ECE convention protocol on SO_2 in July 1985, citing "technological problems" relating to its heavy dependence on lignite. Greece argued that its sulphur emissions were "insignificant" by comparison to other countries.[22] Greece had already reduced its SO_2 emissions by 10% between 1980 and 1983, but development plans involve a rapid and substantial increase in energy generation. Greece anticipates no change.

Ireland

As the westernmost landmass in Europe, as one of Europe's least industrialized countries, and with rates of SO_2 emission and deposition among the lowest in Europe, Ireland barely seems to have an acid pollution problem. The acidity of Irish rain appears to be increasing only slightly: a July 1984 report by the government environmental agency An Foras Forbortha noted that acidity in rainfall had increased over four 5-year periods from pH 5.9 to 5.5 A team from Trinity College, Dublin, revealed in December 1984 that samples taken at Glencree in County Wicklow over a period of ten months had revealed three acid rainstorms strong enough to cause nutrient leaching from soils.

But while Ireland cut its SO_2 emissions by more than a third between 1980 and 1985, emissions are projected to increase by 82% by 1995, a net increase of 15% since 1980. (Only Portugal is likely to see a bigger increase in that time.) The main source of the problem is a new coal-fired power station at Moneypoint (near Ennis in Country Clare). Burning coal with a sulphur content of 1.6%, Moneypoint's two tall stacks will disperse 65,000 tonnes of SO_2 to the winds. This will more than double the previous SO_2 output of the Irish Electricity Board (ESB) and increase total Irish emissions by more than a third. The ESB defends its decision not to fit emission controls to the station on the grounds of insufficient data and the questionable efficacy of controls, and argues that controls would increase electricity rates by 20%.[23] The Irish government admits that, once it runs out of the sulphur-free natural gas that currently generates 50% of Irish electricity, the need to use different fuels will lead to more rises in SO_2 emissions. For the time being, though, Ireland only generates 1% of total Community SO_2 emissions. It argues that committing itself to a 30% reduction would have no measurable benefit for the European environment, and would have adverse consequences for the Irish economy.

Dublin still suffers the effects of a problem long settled in many other EC cities: pollution from coal burned in domestic fireplaces. About a third of the Irish population of 4.5 million lives in and around Dublin, burning about 350,000 tonnes of coal every year. Most of this is bituminous, which produces 45 kg (100 lbs) of smoke, ash and SO_2 per tonne of coal burned. The EC standard for smog is 250 micrograms/cu m. A November 1988 smog in Dublin was so severe that smoke levels rose to 1,700 micrograms/cu m, nearly seven times the accepted level.[24] This prompted environmental activists to distribute hundreds of free surgical masks, and led to calls from opposition politicians for emergency action. The passage of the 1987 Air Pollution Act – which has designated several smoke control areas – may clean up the smogs. Until they are controlled, acid smogs remain a constant danger for Dubliners during the winter months.

Italy
Italy emits 3.15 million tonnes of SO_2 per year (1983 figures), making it the third largest source of EC emissions, after the United Kingdom and Spain. Much of that pollution is concentrated in northern industrial centres like Milan, Turin and Genoa. Although 70% of Italian emissions are redeposited within its borders, air pollution has only recently become a public issue. Italy imports about 80% of its energy, most of that in the form of oil. Italian plans to expand nuclear power were overturned by a November 1987 referendum in which an 80% majority voted against further spending on nuclear power. Months before, the Italian Greens sent thirteen deputies and two senators to parliament, and embarked on a programme to raise public awareness of environmental problems. Since then, the issue of acid pollution has taken on a new prominence.

Few studies have been made into possible environmental damage in Italy. Lake acidification has been reported, as has some forest damage. Northern Italy, including the Po Valley, is at particular risk because of the proximity of industry. Dry deposition is thought to be the critical factor in the Po Valley and wet deposition in Alpine regions. The combined effects of dry deposited air pollutants and a damp sea climate are visible in Venice, where monuments, buildings and works of art are being damaged by corrosive air and water, and an international effort has been launched to save the cultural treasures of the city.

Luxembourg

Luxembourg is by far the smallest member state of the EC, which is probably why it receives more sulphur from outside its borders (73%) than any West European country except Switzerland and Austria. Between 1980 and 1985, it reduced its SO_2 emissions by 43%, and plans a further 14% reduction (over 1980) by 1990, taking its emissions to barely 10,000 tonnes. In August 1984, a nationwide survey of Luxembourg's forests revealed that just under a fifth of the total area was damaged, and about 4% was badly damaged. Worst affected were stands of mature trees, of which almost 30% were damaged. Continuous observations of fifteen selected stands of spruce on particularly exposed sites from September 1983 to September 1984 revealed that the proportion of damaged trees increased from about 5% to more than half. [25]

The Netherlands

The Netherlands is the fourth biggest recipient of sulphur (71%) in Europe. Although Dutch SO_2 emissions fell from 900,000 tonnes in 1965 to 315,000 tonnes in 1983, lakes and forests have been damaged. A 1982 survey of seventy lakes in the south-eastern Netherlands found that fifty-six were acidified. A 1984 survey by the Dutch Forestry Service catalogued the extent of forest damage in 2,800 sites over a total land area of 281,000 hectares (695,000 acres), amounting to 85% of all Dutch woodlands. Just over half the trees were considered healthy; about 40% showed signs of damage but were expected to recover; about 8% were seriously damaged (only partial recovery likely), and 1.5% were irreparably damaged. Coniferous species – particularly the Scots pine – were the most seriously damaged. The major conclusion of the survey was that there was a clear link between tree damage and the vulnerability of the soil to acidification. Trees growing on thin sandy soils were less healthy than those on clay soils.

The Netherlands joined the 30% Club in 1984, undertaking to reduce its SO_2 emissions by 40% by 1994. It planned to do this by making 90% FGD compulsory for all coal-fired power stations by

1990. Between 1980 and 1983 it reduced SO_2 emissions by 35%, and now plans to have reduced them by 51% by 1995. Seen in a longer time frame, the Dutch achievement is even more impressive: emissions in 1983 were down 65% on 1965, and they are planned to be down 74% by 1995.

Portugal

Underdeveloped Portugal has relatively modest SO_2 emissions by EC standards – about 305,000 tonnes in 1983.[26] With a Gross Domestic Product (GDP) lower than any of its European partners ($3,900 per capita in 1987, well below the EC average of nearly $13,000), with most of its people living in rural areas (nearly 70%, higher than any other EC country and compared to 8% of Britons), and with a fifth of its workforce reliant on agriculture, Portugal is still some way from the kind of industrialization that gives rise to air pollution. But this is changing rapidly. Industry has grown at 10% annually for the last decade, and the Portuguese economy is now growing faster than that of any other EC country.[27] One consequence is that Portuguese SO_2 emissions grew by 15% between 1980 and 1983, and NO_x emissions by 16%. Little research has yet been done on the potential effects, but the prospects for acid pollution are greatest in the north because about 75% of Portugal's industry is situated within a 30-mile (50-km) radius of Oporto.

West Germany

Acid rain is a major policy issue in West Germany, prompted partly by the impact of the Greens, but mainly by the only too visible damage to forests. Forests are part of the German psyche – the Norway spruce *picea abies* (the *Tannenbaum* of Christmas carols) is almost a national tree. The Germans also have a long and productive tradition of forest science. University instruction in forestry has been available since the early eighteenth century; foresters from all over Europe depended on German forestry instruction for much of the nineteenth century,[28] when damage caused to German forests by air pollution was first recorded. Known as "smoke damage" because it was particularly visible in areas close to firing and industrial plants, it was found to result from flue gases. Fir dieback – mainly on the fringes of fir tree forests – has been recorded for over 200 years.

During the 1970s, and particularly since 1976, new forms of damage appeared, initially reported on sensitive firs in the south. An outbreak of fir dieback in 1972 was followed by more severe damage in the drought year of 1976. In 1982, after years of denying that acid pollution was a problem, the West German government was shocked into a rapid change of policy by the news that three out of four Norway spruce were damaged or dying, and that the species was close to extinction. "More than just trees are dying in the Black Forest", reported the *New York Times* in May 1984.

> As fir needles turn yellow and spruce branches sag limply, the industrial poisoning of West Germany's forests is assuming the dimensions of a spiritual, as well as an environmental catastrophe. . .The news that the trees are dying has lent West Germany's political debate fresh apocalyptic tones. Forest angst blends with fears about nuclear war.[29]

At the Stockholm conference in June 1982, West German Interior Minister Gerhart Baum called on all states to fight air pollution at source, and announced that West Germany was undertaking to halve its SO_2 emissions. By 1984 the Federal Interior Ministry was warning that economic damage worth several thousand million Deutschmarks per year would result if damage to forests continued to spread. As well as irreplaceable ecological losses, the loss of recreational value could have serious economic consequences. Acting vigorously to stave off *Waldsterben* (forest death), West Germans have since become among the most vocal supporters of EC action to control acid pollution. A 1984 Ministry of the Interior report noted:

> There has been a drastic increase in the amount of damage to forests in the Federal Republic. The new type of damage cannot be categorized according to previous experience. It occurs in areas distant from emission sources and, in the case of fir trees, damage has been reported from the centre of their range of distribution. Since then, all tree species have been affected.[30]

The findings of the report were based on a nationwide survey in

1983 which concluded that 34% of West German forests were affected. This was a dramatic increase on the year before, when a survey revealed that 7.6% of forest land was damaged.

But worse news was to come. A survey in mid-October 1984 found that 50.2% of West German forests were affected by air pollutants.[31] Had the summer of 1984 been hotter, the figure would probably have been even higher, since hot, dry weather promotes the spread of damage. Of the older trees (more than sixty years old), 82% of the firs and spruces, 73% of the pines, 50% of the beeches and 43% of the oaks were damaged. More trees than are normally allowed to be felled in one year had to be classified as dead or dying and taken away. In the central and southern states, where the largest forested areas are found and where forestry has the greatest economic and aesthetic value, the damaged area nearly doubled between 1983 and 1985. Among the worst affected areas were the Fitchtelgebirge and Bayerischer Wald in Bavaria (where nearly 70% of the trees were dying, leading to warnings that alpine forests could lose their capacity to prevent avalanches); the Schwarzwald (Black Forest) in Baden-Württemberg, the Böhmer Wald (Bohemian Forest) on the West German/Czech border, and the Erzgebirge, on the East German/Czech border. By 1985, the percentage of damaged forests had risen still further to 52%.[32]

Perhaps the most seriously affected region is the Harz, a forested mountain area near the border with East Germany. It is popular with hikers and skiers and contains nature and health resorts. With no industries or other evident sources of pollution, the Harz was long regarded as one of the cleanest regions in West Germany. But 200 km (125 miles) to the west is the Ruhr, the German industrial heartland, with its massive emissions of gases, carbon compounds, metals and particles. This is carried by westerly winds to the forests, soils and waters of the Harz. Twenty years ago there were no visible signs of damage in the Harz. Today damage is spreading rapidly. Land above 600 m (2,000 ft) is already seriously affected, and evidence of damage is spreading to lower land. Large areas of forest are dead or dying from nutrient deficiency, aluminium poisoning, dying roots and impaired vitality. The Harz is also an important freshwater reservoir for northern Germany. The water is still drinkable, because the buffering systems in the ground can still neutralize most of the acidic deposition, but the buffering capacity is weakening. Little decomposition takes place, and dead trees, branches and twigs lie largely unaffected on the ground.

Watercourses, lakes and groundwater in these forested areas are similarly affected. Surveys from 1981 to 1983 found far higher acid levels than usual in the unpolluted upper reaches of free-flowing waters with low lime content, particularly in the upland areas of lower mountain ranges. In some cases, levels are higher than those found in Scandinavia. High aluminium concentrations have also been found in these watercourses. Acidification has even been reported in naturally acidic moor ponds and heath lakes, where pH values have fallen by 1–2 points since the 1950s. The quality of groundwater has not been thoroughly surveyed, but there is evidence of high levels of heavy metals in Bavarian groundwater, and acidification of water in the Taunus and Hunsruck mountains.

Annual SO_2 emissions in West Germany in 1980 were 3.2 million tonnes. The Ordinance on Large Combustion Installations – which applies to the 1,500 power stations with a capacity of more than 50 MW – was passed in 1983, aimed at halving SO_2 emissions by 1993. By 1985, West German emissions had fallen to 2.4 million tonnes, a reduction of 25%. Current projections put emissions in 1995 at 1.1 million tonnes, a fall of 66% on 1980 figures. By 1986, power plants with a total capacity of 12,000 MW (equivalent to six large power stations) had been fitted with FGD, and FGD for a further 30,000 MW was on order or under construction. These plants must also be retrofitted with NO_x flue gas scrubbers. Six selective catalytic reduction (SCR) installations were also in operation, and SCR for a further 12,000 MW was on order or under construction.[33]

Perhaps the most controversial aspect of West Germany's acid pollution problem has been the struggle to deal with vehicle emissions. NO_x and HC are central to the problem of forest damage and forest death in West Germany, so any strategy to solve the problem must include a substantial cut in motor vehicle exhaust emissions. But it has also meant taking on the powerful West German car industry – and the West German motorist. Autobahn speed limits arouse the same kind of passions in West Germany as gun control laws do in the United States. Most West German motorists regard any attempts to curb their impulses behind the wheel of a BMW or

Mercedes as an attack on their civil liberties. The speed limit issue was first raised by environmentalists when it was apparent how badly damaged the forests were. West Germany has since been more active than any other European nation – except perhaps Switzerland – in promoting regulations on car exhaust gases.

Spain

With estimated annual SO_2 emissions in 1985 of 3.25 million tonnes, Spain is the second biggest source of SO_2 in the EC. Nearly two-thirds of its deposition is self-inflicted, and only 18% comes from foreign sources,[34] although Spain's Instituto Nacional de Meteorologia argues that, because there has been virtually no research, there is too little data on air pollutants to be sure. Initial studies in the early 1980s suggested that several hundred thousand hectares of forest were already damaged, especially in the Cornisa Cantábrica on the north coast. This is downwind of the major industrial areas of Bilbao and Avilés, and near the power stations of Serchs (Barcelona), Andorra (Teruel) and El Serrallo (Castellón). There were reports from the Bilbao area as early as 1970 of householders finding small holes in clothes hung out to dry. A 1982 report estimated that industry in Avilés alone generated 24,000 tonnes of SO_2 annually.[35]

High levels of atmospheric sulphur pollution have also been recorded in San Juan de Nieva where the biggest single source of SO_2 in the region is the Ensidesa steelworks. A commission set up to study pollution in the forests of El Maestrazgo and Els Ports de Tortosa-Beseit, which spread over three provinces, suggested that emissions from Andorra might be affecting these forests.[36] Over the last two years, Spain has been expanding its National Air Pollution Monitoring Network in order to measure SO_2 and NO_x more accurately.[37]

Spain ratified the ECE convention in June 1982. Despite its substantial emissions, it argued that transboundary air and acid pollution was less of a problem in Spain than in other countries, but admitted in 1985 that its accession to the EC in January 1986 would likely involve a "difficult and costly adaptation" of its environmental policies.[38] It currently projects a modest 6% reduction in emissions by 1992,[39] suggesting that it will need to make some fairly substantial

Table 6.3: SO$_2$ emissions in non-EC Western Europe (in thousand tonnes)

	1980	Most recent figure 1985	1986	% change since 1980	Projected reductions by 1995
Finland	584	370		−37	−54
Sweden	483	272		−44	−68
Austria	354	170		−52	−72*
Norway	141	100†		−29	−50*
Switzerland	126		63	−50	−54 (1990)

* = at most (may be less)
† = preliminary

Source: United Nations, *National Strategies and Policies for Air Pollution Abatement* (New York: United Nations, 1987).

policy changes in order to meet the terms of the ECE Convention or the various EC directives.

Scandinavia and the rest of Western Europe

No two countries have campaigned so assiduously for controls on acid pollution as Sweden and Norway. Situated downwind from Europe's major industrial centres, they have been on the receiving end of acid pollution for decades. Swedish and Norwegian scientists were the first successfully to draw international attention to the problem, and during the 1950s and 1960s undertook much of the research into the chemistry of acid pollution. During the 1970s and 1980s, both countries campaigned vigorously to win international agreement on the control of acid pollution. Relatively lightly industrialized, deeply concerned about social welfare, dominated for most of the century by social democratic governments, and enjoying standards of living among the highest in the world, the Scandinavians have felt particularly concerned about the problem of acid pollution. The stunning success of the Swedish Green Party at the September 1988 election (they won twenty seats, becoming the first new party to enter the Swedish parliament in seventy years), reflects Sweden's heightened environmental awareness.

Scandinavian concern about acid rain was one of the spurs to the 1972 Stockholm Conference; equal concern about the lack of real progress was the spur to the 1982 Stockholm Conference on acid rain. Since acid damage was first confirmed in the region in the 1950s, the level of damage in Norway and Sweden has worsened, and damage has been reported in Finland. All three countries have thin soils with poor buffering capacity, are well endowed with lakes, rivers and forests, receive much of their precipitation as snow, and see forests as a major economic resource. As the source of much of Europe's pulp and paper, they have been called "Europe's wood-shed". West Germany and the United Kingdom are particularly dependent on Scandinavian forest products.

All three of these Scandinavian countries are also net receivers of air pollutants, but have made substantial reductions in their own emissions (see Table 6.3). Sweden and Norway have argued that reductions under the 30% Club should be regarded as the first step towards really substantial SO_2 and NO_x reductions, and plan to meet the goal much earlier than 1993. Norway is pressing for international acceptance of a goal of a 50% reduction of SO_2 emissions in ten years. By 1995, Sweden, Finland and Norway plan to have reduced their emissions by 68%, 54% and 50% respectively.

All three countries are trying to reduce their dependence on imported oil. All three have energy conservation programmes; Swedish energy consumption for domestic and commercial heating was cut by half between 1976 (when its conservation programme began) and 1985. Norway is planning to expand its already heavy reliance (49% in 1980) on hydro- and geo-thermal power. Swedish reliance on liquid fuels has fallen from 64% in 1980 to 40% today.[40] This has been achieved with a doubling of its reliance on solid fuels and nuclear power. New legislation on coal combustion that was adopted early in 1984 requires all large installations in Sweden to fit efficient FGD equipment. Two FGD plants are now in operation, and another five are planned. For smaller plants, where FGD is not economically feasible, emissions standards require the use of fluidized beds or other advanced combustion techniques, or the use of low-sulphur fuels. Economic incentives (including government grants of up to 75% of the installation costs) are being used to encourage the implementation of emission controls.

Sweden

Sweden receives about 58% of its sulphur from abroad, (mainly from the United Kingdom, Belgium, the Netherlands, East and West Germany, Poland and the Soviet Union). The last Ice Age left it with thin soils and little natural buffering capacity, making large parts of the country sensitive to acid damage. Sweden's active role in international emission control initiatives has been prompted mainly by concern for the future of forestry, agriculture and human health. Sweden has about 23 million hectares (57 million acres) of forest, and forest products are Sweden's largest source of export earnings, accounting for 25% of total earnings and for about 100,000 jobs.

Reports of Swedish forest damage in the summer of 1983 prompted a systematic but limited inventory by the Swedish Board of Forestry. This revealed damage in the south and south west, the areas with the highest incidence of air pollution deposition from Europe. Even the preliminary results indicated that 240 forest stands in eleven counties were damaged, more than half of them extensively with every tenth tree damaged or dying.[41] Damaged trees were more common in old forests, and the damage was greatest on the western and south western edges of forests – pointing to air pollutants as the cause – and increased above altitudes of 100 m (330 ft).

In 1982, there were 18,000 acidified lakes in Sweden (twice as many as in 1975), signs of groundwater acidification in its western parts, and warnings (since confirmed) of future forest damage.[42] Acidification damage has recently been identified in northern mountain areas. In the winters of 1979–80 and 1983–84, snow in the far north of these regions was acid, and sensitive waters were damaged. Recent estimates show that 90,000 km (56,000 miles) of running waters have pH values low enough to cause ecological damage. Sulphur is the main cause of surface water acidification. Even if sulphur deposition was reduced by 30–50%, it would not be enough to protect these sensitive waters. A reduction of 70–80% would be needed in the southern parts of Sweden to do any good.

Groundwater acidification is an important issue, particularly as 3.7 million people (close to half the population) draw their daily drinking water from groundwater supplies, whether directly or through waterworks. Another 2 million Swedes rely on groundwater at their rural cottages, where many spend the summers. In the worst affected areas (south and south west), acidification is so bad that copper piping in water systems has corroded. The annual cost of damage from acid groundwater has been estimated at $120 million.[43]

Sweden halved its SO_2 emissions between 1976 and 1985, at an annual cost of about $100 to $120 million (mainly the cost of buying low-sulphur oil instead of 2.5%-sulphur oil). The first restrictions were introduced in 1969, but more comprehensive measures came into force in 1976, including use of low-sulphur oil (1% sulphur is the maximum limit), reduced industrial emissions, and energy conservation. In 1985 the Swedish parliament adopted a target of a 65% reduction in SO_2 by 1995. Sweden also plans a 30% reduction of NO_x emissions, which account for 30% of the acid in Swedish deposition, and is particularly critical in acid surges during the spring snow melt. Catalytic converters and unleaded petrol were introduced on a voluntary basis to 1987 and 1988 model cars, and from 1989 they will be compulsory.

Norway
The proportion of imported sulphur in Norwegian air (63%) is among the highest in the world, and Norway's domestic SO_2 emission figure of 100,000 tonnes (1985) is one of the lowest in Europe. The United Kingdom is the source of 10–16% of this sulphur. Norway's mountainous west coast is a major factor in the destructive power of Norwegian acid rain – prevailing westerly and southerly winds meet daily with low pressure weather systems, producing rainfall that scavenges pollutants from the air.[44] Norway receives levels of acid pollutants comparable to the most heavily polluted industrial regions of Europe, with the added complication that its granite bedrock – like that of Sweden – has little neutralizing capacity.

Half of Norway's precipitation is in the form of snow, which creates particularly critical problems during the spring melt. The snow-melt of 1975, for example, killed large numbers of fish in southern Norway's Tovdal River. Recent studies reveal that fish populations have been lost in 2,650 lakes in an area of 33,000 sq km (1,300 sq miles). Salmon have gone from most of southern Norway's rivers, and brown trout populations have declined, with marked consequences for the popular sports fishing industry.

Most of Norway's domestic sulphur emissions come from the combustion of coal and oil in industry, domestic heating and smelting. (Almost all Norwegian electricity is generated by hydro-power.) In an attempt to reduce NO_x, all filling stations with more than one pump have had to offer lead-free petrol since July 1987, and lead-free petrol will be available at all stations from 1992. Norway is also considering the long-term introduction of FGD, and has actively helped existing sources to control pollution by offering long-term loans and tax concessions. But with so much of its sulphur imported, Norway argues that there is little more it can do domestically to control acid pollution. Indeed, Norwegian industrialists have in the past resisted strong sulphur controls as expensive tokenism.[45] Hence Norway's active role in international initiatives.

Finland

Finland is the most heavily forested country in the world. About 70% (23 million hectares/57 million acres) of its land area is forest, mainly coniferous. Forest products account for 53% of its export earnings and for more than 500,000 jobs. Despite this, acid pollution has only relatively recently become a national public issue. Finland was one of the last European countries to pass clean air legislation (in 1982), and barely any scientific surveys have been made of the effects of air pollution. A 1984 survey – the first of its kind – revealed acid damage in a number of lakes near Helsinki: 107 lakes were investigated and half of them, mostly small forest lakes, were found to be either suffering from severe acidification or to have such a low buffering capacity that all their fish would be gone within a year. Lakes with a pH of 4.5 are already devoid of fish, just as in Norway and Sweden, and high aluminium concentrations have also been found. The lakes in the survey were subject to some Finnish industrial and urban emissions, but most of the sulphur (55%) comes from Europe, including Sweden. South-eastern Finland also receives pollution from the Leningrad area.

There have been no comprehensive surveys of Finnish forests, but damage has been found in the southern and south western parts of the country. Researchers at the University of Helsinki and Oulu University have been investigating atmospheric pollution trends, the sensitivity of pine seedlings to pollution, and the effects of SO_2 on pine needles. If air pollution levels continue unchecked, widespread forest damage is predicted for the 1990s.[46]

Austria
Austria was one of the founding signatories of the 30% Club, and between 1980 and 1985 it reduced its SO_2 emissions by 52%, more than any other country in the world. It plans a further 20% reduction by 1995, putting it ahead of even West Germany and Sweden. The major incentive has been forest damage. Forest covers more than 45% of Austria, and accounts for about 10% of export revenues. By 1985, about 16% (600,000 hectares/1.48 million acres) was reported damaged, and there was a real danger that Austria would annually lose timber worth an estimated $166 million.

Austria sends out 60% of its annual SO_2 emissions of 170,000 tonnes, while 76% of its SO_2 deposits are received. Fluidized bed combustion systems have been installed in several power plants, and FGD and denitrification equipment is required in all new plants. About 70% of Austrian NO_x emissions are thought to be caused by road traffic, so in August 1983 it became the second European country after West Germany to announce that it would introduce unleaded petrol. From 1 October 1985 unleaded petrol was available at all petrol stations; at the same time, the tax on unleaded fuel was cut and the tax on leaded fuel raised. Austria's announcement of a switch to unleaded petrol came after a meeting between the Austrian and West German health ministers, and reflected a concern equal to that of West Germany about the effects of acid pollution on forests.

Switzerland

Swiss SO_2 emissions (63,000 tonnes in 1986) are among the lowest in Europe, but Switzerland receives more sulphur (78%) from outside its borders than any country in Europe. This has serious implications for its forests, which cover more than a quarter of its land area. In 1983 a quarter of the firs and 10% of the spruces in flatland cantons died, and 8–14% of Swiss forests were thought to be damaged. Early in 1984, the Swiss government allocated $13 million for measures to combat forest damage and forest death. Since then, 12 million sick trees (14% of Swiss forests) have been felled.[47] According to a survey of 27,000 trees in mid-1984 by the Swiss Forestry Research Institute, a third of Swiss trees were damaged, and 8% seriously damaged or dying. Only on 2% of the trees could the damage be directly attributed to insects, fungi or snowfalls. The worst damage was in the southern Alpine cantons of Grisons and Valais, where 50–60% of the trees were affected.[48]

Switzerland is a 30% Club member, and now has the strictest vehicle exhaust control regulations in Europe. On 1 January 1985, Switzerland introduced two new regulations to control NO_x emissions. Firstly, only unleaded petrol could be imported or delivered by Swiss refineries; since 1 July 1986 only unleaded petrol has been sold. Secondly, speed limits on motorways were reduced from 130 kph to 120 kph (80 to 75 mph), on ordinary open highways from 100 kph to 80 kph (62 to 50 mph), and in built up areas from 60 kph to 50 kph (37 to 31 mph). Other measures being considered included more efficient control of vehicle exhausts, more efficient control of home heating installations, and reductions of the sulphur content of light heating oil. Between 1980 and 1986, Switzerland halved its SO_2 emissions, and it plans another 4% reduction by 1990.

NOTES

1. McCormick, John, *The Global Environmental Movement:* (London: Belhaven Press, 1989).
2. Wetstone, Gregory S. and Armin Rosencranz, *Acid Rain in Europe and North America: National Responses to an International Problem* (Washington, DC: Environmental Law Institute, 1983).
3. Haigh, Nigel, "Devolved responsibility and centralisation: Effects of EEC environmental policy", in *Public Administration* 64:2 (Summer

1986), pp. 197–207.
4. Elsom, Derek, *Atmospheric Pollution* (Oxford: Basil Blackwell, 1987).
5. For details see Haigh, Nigel, *EEC Environmental Policy and Britain* (London: Longman, 1987).
6. Organization for Economic Cooperation and Development, *The State of the Environment 1985* (Paris: OECD, 1985).
7. United Nations Economic Commission for Europe, *National Strategies and Policies for Air Pollution Abatement* (New York: United Nations, 1987).
8. See note 7.
9. Pallemaerts, Marc, "Belgium sits on the fence", in *Acid News 5*, December 1984.
10. Agren, Christer, "Denmark: 30% reduction in sulphur emissions proposed", in *Acid News 2*, March 1984.
11. IEA/OECD, "Energy balances and IEA country submissions, 1983", in Brackley, Peter, *Acid Deposition and Vehicle Emissions: European Environmental Pressure on Britain* (Aldershot: Gower Publishing Co. Ltd, 1987).
12. Brackley, see note 11.
13. UNECE, see note 7.
14. Brackley, see note 11.
15. OECD, *OECD Environmental Data, Compendium 1985* (Paris: OECD 1985).
16. Office National des Forêts, *Réseau ONF d'Observation du Dépérissement des Forêts Attribué à la Pollution Atmosphérique* (Paris: ONF, 1985).
17. Reichfelt, Professor W, in *Landschaft & Stadt* 15, 1983, quoted in *Acid News 2*, March 1984.
18. Guyotat, Régis, "Rheims's future written in stone", in *Le Monde*, 15 December 1988. Reproduced in *Guardian Weekly*, 29 January 1989.
19. Report of the Greek delegation (unpublished). Presented at Conference on the Acidification of the Environment, Stockholm, June 1982.
20. *International Herald Tribune*, 4 January 1984.
21. *The Times*, 18 July 1984.
22. Greek report (unpublished) to the Third Meeting of the Executive Board of the Convention on Long-Range Transboundary Air Pollution, Helsinki, July 1985.
23. Chase, William, "Ireland: hoping for strong winds", in *Acid News 5*, December 1984.
24. *New York Times*, 18 January 1989.

25. Direction des Eaux et Fôrets, *Entwicklung der neuartigen Waldschaden in Luxembourg* (Luxembourg: DEF, 1984).
26. UNECE, see note 7.
27. "Another New World: a survey of Portugal" in *The Economist*, 30 May–3 June 1988.
28. McCormick, see note 1.
29. *New York Times*, 12 May 1984.
30. Federal Ministry of the Interior, *Report of the Causes and Prevention of Damage to Forests, Waters and Buildings by Air Pollution in the Federal Republic of Germany* (Bonn: Ministry of the Interior, 1984).
31. Federal Ministry of Food, Agriculture and Forestry, *1984 Forest Damage Survey* (Bonn: Federal Ministry of Food, Agriculture and Forestry, 1984).
32. Federal Ministry of Food, Agriculture and Forestry, *1985 Forest Damage Survey* (Bonn: Federal Ministry of Food, Agriculture and Forestry, 1985).
33. UNECE, see note 7.
34. EMEP, 1981.
35. Quoted by *La Vanguardia*, 29 April 1984.
36. *La Vanguardia*, 23 October 1984.
37. UNECE, see note 7.
38. Spanish report (unpublished) to the Third Meeting of the Executive Board of the Convention on Long-Range Transboundary Air Pollution, Helsinki, July 1985.
39. UNECE, see note 7.
40. UNECE, see note 7.
41. Environment 82 Committee, *Acidification Today and Tomorrow* (Stockholm: Ministry of Agriculture, 1982).
42. See note 41.
43. Swedish Environmental Protection Board, based on research by the Corrosion Institute.
44. Wetstone and Rosencranz, see note 2.
45. See note 2.
46. Landin, Bo, "Finland: acidification diagnosed", in *Acid News 4*, October 1984.
47. Swedish Delegation in Geneva, and *Dagens Nyheter*, Stockholm.
48. Bundesamt für Forstwesen, Ergebnisse der SANASILVA Waldschadeninventur, 1984.

7. North America – A Fall-out among Friends

Each year, the Canadian prime minister and the president of the United States meet to discuss matters of mutual interest to their two countries. These summits between close allies are generally affable, but during the Reagan years there was one issue on which the two leaders repeatedly disagreed: acid pollution.

In 1980, more than 50 million tonnes of SO_2 and NO_x were released over North America, most coming from the industrial mid-western United States, and much of it falling on eastern Canada. In 1980, Canada and the United States committed themselves to reaching a joint agreement on the problem. In June 1982 Canada offered to reduce its SO_2 emissions by half if the United States agreed to do the same. The United States refused. In February 1984 the Canadian government told the United States of its "deep disappointment" that US plans on transboundary pollution failed to include any action to reduce SO_2 emissions. Early in 1984, Canada's ambassador to the United States noted that the environment was "the longest-standing irritant" in relations between the two countries.[1] In 1986, Ronald Reagan finally agreed to spend $2.5 billion on research, and in 1987 he agreed to consider a bi-lateral accord on acid rain.

In January 1989, President Reagan left office with his acid rain policy virtually intact. For eight years he had stalled, made excuses, hedged, made non-specific promises, and generally avoided the issue – much to the frustration of the Canadians. At no time had the Reagan administration shown any sign that it proposed taking concrete action to curb pollutive emissions. Instead, it consistently argued that there was too little conclusive evidence that SO_2 and NO_x emissions caused acid pollution, and too few conclusive signs of damage. William Ruckelshaus, former administrator of the Environmental Protection Agency (EPA), said in March 1985 that he did not see much prospect for a change in US policy until there were more reports of acid damage in the United States. In fact, it only took a change of administration, because in June 1989, George Bush announced plans for major SO_2 and NO_x reductions.

United States: two out of three states affected

With total annual SO_2 emissions of 20.8 million tonnes, the United States is second only to the Soviet Union as a source of SO_2. The biggest producers (in order of volume) are the states of Ohio, Pennsylvania, Indiana, Illinois, Missouri, Wisconsin, Kentucky, Florida, West Virginia and Tennessee; together, they account for two-thirds of all SO_2 emissions east of the Rockies.[2] The most polluted states are those in the north-east, but there is growing evidence of damage in the south, south-west and north-west. A total of thirty-seven states are now known either to be vulnerable to acid pollution or already damaged by it.

Rainfall with a pH of 4.0 and 4.5 is commonplace in the eastern United States, and individual rainstorms with a pH below 3.0 have been recorded. (An unofficial pH of 2.0 was recorded during a 1978 storm over Wheeling, West Virginia.[3]) The National Academy of Sciences estimates that damage worth $5 billion or more is inflicted every year in in the eastern states alone, where thin or sandy soils and limited buffering capacity make the soils suscep- tible to damage. In 1981, the Academy warned that prevailing rates of SO_2 and NO_x emissions could lead to a doubling in the number of acidified lakes by the end of the decade.[4] In more than 200 lakes in the Adirondack mountains of New York state, fish had already disappeared by 1982.[5] The EPA estimates that 326 lakes in the north-east are already acidic, and that many more could turn acid in the next fifty years.[6] Many high mountain streams in Pennsylvania have lost their buffering capacity, and lakes as far west as Minnesota have been damaged. The EPA estimated in a 1988 report that farmers could lose as much as 30% of their potential crop from ozone pollution, even at levels that comply with federal standards. The EPA concluded that the United States was losing crops worth $2.5 to $3 billion annually.[7]

Unlike Europe, where forest damage has been recorded at all altitudes, forest decline in the United States has so far been mainly restricted to high ground. Dr Arthur Johnson, a soil scientist at the University of Pennsylvania, noted in 1984 that "in a large number of cases, the growth of forest trees has been substantially less than expected during the past fifteen to twenty-five years. [In a few cases] mortality has been substantially greater than expected".[8] Acid pollution is suspected of killing red spruce trees on high mountain slopes in Vermont,[9] and damaging white pines, poplars, sycamore, and maples in the Ohio Valley.[10] In upper New York state, drinking water has been found with lead levels that exceed federal standards and children have been found with excessive lead levels in their blood.[11] Fish with mercury levels that exceed US safety standards have been caught in New York and Minnesota. In 1984, the Statue of Liberty was partly dismantled for restoration; nearly a century in the polluted, salty air of New York City had caused severe corrosion to its iron frame and copper cladding. In 1988, the president of the Fine Arts Federation of New York described the facade of the New York Public Library on Fifth Avenue as a "chemical laboratory", under attack from distant power plants and nearby road traffic.[12]

Rainfall in the south has become increasingly acidic since the 1950s, and dry sulphur deposition is projected to increase in most southern states by the mid-1990s.[13] Up to 60% of the sulphate deposition in the region is locally generated.[14] The flush of acids that follows the spring snow-melt in West Virginia delays fish restocking in mountain streams. On Mt Mitchell in North Carolina, vegetation is unable to reproduce itself. Mature red spruce trees are losing up to 90% of their foliage. Pine trees in the Great Smoky mountains have virtually stopped growing during the past 20–25 years, according to an analysis of annual growth rings by researchers from the Oak Ridge National laboratory. In the twenty-one-year period from 1962 to 1983, tree ring growth was equal to that over the four-year period of 1958 to 1961.[15]

Studies in Virginia's Shenandoah National Park have shown that soils are losing their buffering capacity, and concentrations of toxic metals lethal to fish are leaching into streams. In Florida, as many as 4,600 lakes are considered susceptible to acidification because of the low buffering capacity of the sandy soils on which they lie. Scientists from the University of Florida at Gainesville note that the acidity of rainfall in Florida has increased markedly in the past twenty-five years. They put the annual average pH level in the northern three-quarters of the state at 4.7, although readings as low as 3.8 have been returned.[16]

There is evidence of actual or possible acid pollution damage or acidification in every state west of the Rockies. Virtually every mountain range in the region is sensitive, and acid deposition has been recorded in the Rockies themselves, in the Sierra Nevada and the Cascade mountains, and in national parks such as Yosemite, King's Canyon, Olympic and Yellowstone. Many of the 10,000 lakes above 2,900 (9,500 ft) in the Rocky Mountains are thought to be susceptible to acid pollution.[17] Rain measured at two sites in Wyoming and Colorado has already been found to be ten times more acid than unpolluted rainwater. In isolated mountain lakes in Colorado, no trout have hatched for two years.[18]

Research by the Environmental Defense Fund (EDF) in 1984 indicated that about 70% of total SO_2 emissions in the Rockies came from smelters, and about 25% from coal-fired power plants. EDF also warned that there were likely to be large increases in SO_2 and NO_x emissions as new sources of pollution emerged over the next 10–20 years. These included new coal-fired power stations, synthetic fuel projects, fertilizer plants and natural gas processing plants in the Rockies themselves. There were fears in the mid-1980s that huge sulphur emissions would come from a new copper smelter at Nacozari, 100 km (60 miles) inside Mexico, and from expansions to a smelter at nearby Cananea.

The United States was already polluting Mexico. Acid pollution and smoke from copper smelters in southern Arizona and New Mexico was regularly being blown south across the border into Mexico during the night and – as winds changed direction – being blown back north during the day. This exchange led to a border environmental agreement between Mexico and the United States in August 1983, by which the EPA and the Mexican Department of Urban Development and Ecology agreed to meet intermittently. In January 1987, the United States and Mexico reached a new agreement under which both sides would stop polluting each other. The relative ease with which the agreement was reached angered the Canadian government, which was still working hard to compel the United States to control pollution in the mid-west.

In California, the major sources of emissions are domestic, mainly from southern California and the San Francisco Bay area. Winds may be able to carry polluted air from southern California 500 km (300 miles) or more into north-western Arizona, site of the Grand Canyon. The winds around San Francisco also blow emissions south-east into the highly productive farmland of the San Joaquin valley. Air masses stagnating in the valley have caused high ozone levels in the Yosemite and Sequoia national parks. The yield of some crops in the San Joaquin valley has already fallen by up to 20%, but there is no clear link yet with acid pollution.

Monitoring projects have recorded some remarkably acid precipitation in California. Droplets in a 1984 winter fog in the town of Corona del Mar (south of Los Angeles) had a pH level of 1.69.[19] At six sites in southern California, pH values below 5.0 were recorded in 1984, and a pH of 3.1 was recorded at Pasadena.[20] Fog with acid levels comparable to concentrated sulphuric acid has been recorded in the Los Angeles basin and the San Francisco Bay area. In the San Bernardino mountains east of Los Angeles, ozone damage to trees is well documented. Harvests of ponderosa pine in the mountains have fallen by 80% since the second world war. The effects of acid pollution prompted the launch in 1984 of a five-year, $18 million monitoring programme, with half the money coming from levies imposed on thirty-five major Californian industrial polluters. The programme set up thirty-six monitoring stations – mostly near Los Angeles and San Francisco and in the Sierra mountains – to establish how acid pollution is formed in the state.

In the Pacific north-west, there are fears that Oregon and Washington – which have acid-sensitive soils – may be vulnerable to acidification. Acid damage would have particularly serious consequences in Oregon, which is heavily reliant on an already ailing timber industry. Most of the pollution is self-generated, but the proximity of Canada introduces an international dimension. Monitoring was disrupted for a while by the huge amounts of sulphur thrown into the atmosphere by the 1980 eruption of Mt St Helens, but non-natural emissions are thought to cause deposition in some urban areas. A 1985 report quoted "solid evidence" of acid deposition in the Cascades (east of Seattle) which, despite the proximity to Mt St Helens, may be linked mainly to non-natural emissions.[21] Rain falling in the Puget Sound area in November 1973 had a pH of 3.8–4.8.

Urban smog – a mixture of SO_2, NO_x, ozone, lead, particulates, and carbon monoxide (CO) – is proving to be a growing problem in the United States. Since the 1970 Clean Air Act was passed, emissions of hydrocarbons (HC) and CO have fallen by 90%, and of NO_x by 75%. But many of the gains are being offset by the rapid growth of road traffic. Between 1977 and 1988, the number of road vehicles grew by 25%,[22] and the number of kilometres travelled per person in private cars grews by 21%.[23] Nowhere is the love-affair between Americans and their cars more obvious than in Los Angeles, a city that still stifles under choking smogs despite improved vehicle exhaust controls, fuel production and industrial pollution management. But it is not alone. The growing use of private cars combined with the heat wave of 1988 to push ozone levels in more than 100 cities beyond EPA recommended levels. By August 1988, the EPA had banned all new construction of major sources of air pollution in Los Angeles, and said it was considering bans on thirteen other urban centres, including Ventura County (California), Denver, East St Louis, Cleveland, Dallas–Fort Worth, Atlanta, and parts of Chicago.[24]

The Reagan years: a legacy of neglect

The major air pollution law in the United States is the Clean Air Act, first passed in 1963, but considerably amended in 1970 to provide a ten-year timetable for reducing air pollution. National air quality standards were to be set and met by 1975, vehicle exhaust standards tightened, emission limits imposed on new industrial sources, and private citizens given the right to sue industry or the government for not complying. Among the pollutants included in the act were SO_2, NO_x, ozone, HC, particulates and lead. By 1977 it was clear that most states would not be able to meet the deadline, so they were changed and vehicle emission standards were eased. Efforts were made in 1988 to strengthen the Act, but came up once again against a coalition of interests which had effectively blocked federal action on acid rain and other forms of air pollution for more than a decade: the electricity and coal industries.

As a public policy issue, acid rain has been a relative late-comer to the United States. Debate over the 1977 amendments to the Clean Air Act all but ignored the issue.[25] The Carter administration argued that better scientific knowledge was needed, but that this should not delay policy responses. In 1980, Congress established a ten-year, multi-agency research programme – the National Acid Precipitation Assessment Program (NAPAP) – to assess the causes and effects of acid precipitation. Between 1982 and 1987, more than $300 million was spent on research under NAPAP, mainly by the EPA, the National Oceanic and Atmospheric Administration (NOAA), and the Departments of Energy, Agriculture, and the Interior.[26]

The Reagan administration for its part argued that "bad science" had led to "economic tragedies",[27] and that pollution control could not come without better evidence. The interests of industry and economic recovery were more important to it than those of the environment lobby. During 1983, however, the Reagan position became markedly less credible with the announcement of the findings of three key committees. The first was a report from the Inter-Agency Task Force on Acid Precipitation (part of NAPAP), arguing that non-natural sources of pollution were probably the major cause of acid deposition and declining pH in the north-eastern United States.

The second report, issued in June 1983 by the National Academy of Sciences, argued that SO_2 emission reductions would lead directly to a reduction in acid deposition. In other words, there was a strong linear relationship between emissions and depositions. The report warned that the picture was "disturbing enough to merit prompt tightening of restrictions on atmospheric emissions from fossil fuels and other large source such as metal smelters and cement manufacture", and that there was a strong case for immediate controls. "If we take the conservative view that we must wait until the scientific knowledge is definitive, the accumulated deposition and damaged environment may reach the point of 'irreversibility'".[28]

The third report, by a White House scientific panel, recommended immediate action to curb sulphur emissions, denied that significantly more scientific certainty would be obtainable in the following few years, and emphasized that years of additional research were unlikely to indicate the need for a different control programme. Recommendations based on imperfect data ran the risk of being in error, the panel concluded, but "recommendations for inaction pending collection of all the desirable data entails even greater risk of damage." It argued that "the benefits of a properly functioning ecosystem are much more than matters of dollars and cents, and are often not appreciated by people unfamiliar with ecology".[29]

President Reagan's environmental policy during the first few years of his administration showed clearly where his priorities lay. In his attempts to cut the federal budget, he reduced the staff of the Energy Department by nearly 23%, and even considered abolishing it altogether.[30] The EPA, which is responsible for administering the Clean Air Act, had its budget cut by 30% and its staff by 23%.[31] Reagan's first appointee as EPA administrator was Anne Gorsuch (later Burford), a former corporate attorney whose clients included many industries hostile to federal environmental regulations. She in turn appointed eleven subordinates who had been lawyers, lobbyists, or consultants for industries regulated by the EPA.[32] Gorsuch herself felt that proposals for controlling acid rain were "blind groping in response to political passion".[33]

Cited for contempt of Congress in 1983, she resigned, to be replaced by William Ruckelshaus, a former EPA administrator widely respected as a moderate. Ruckelshaus regarded acid rain as an EPA priority. President Reagan himself had said that many people, "both here and in Canada, are concerned about the harmful effects that acid rain may be having on lakes and forests", and instructed Ruckelshaus to "meet this issue head-on". These sounded like fighting words, but the 1984–85 Reagan budget still made no mention of acid emission reductions, asking only for more money for research. Spending on acid rain control was being vigorously opposed by the budget-cutting Office of Management and Budget, headed by David Stockman.

Ruckelshaus announced in January 1984 that, while funds for acid rain research would be doubled, no action would be taken on control measures, and that the administration still considered more scientific research necessary before any decisions could be made about concrete measures to cut emissions. This decision, he said, was "rational not irresponsible." He believed his mission entailed stopping Congress from enacting an acid pollution programme that "could create a great deal of social disruption";[34] he strongly favoured a "sensible" acid pollution programme that would balance environmental benefits against "other social goals." Research in 1984 was to include the monitoring of nitrates and sulphates in 3,000 lakes, and in 1985 to survey the scale of damage to forests. Ruckelshaus admitted to the Senate Environment Committee that such research should have begun as much as ten years before.[35] He left the EPA in 1984, having been able to achieve little.

Research was meanwhile supposedly continuing under the auspices of NAPAP, but a 1987 report revealed that the programme had fallen well short of expectations.[36] It had sponsored and conducted scientific research on acid pollution since 1982, but had published nothing of any use to Congress. Congress had required it to issue annual reports with recommendations, but NAPAP argued that knowledge had "not advanced sufficiently to support firm conclusions". Reports missed deadlines because of staff shortages, conflicting staff responsibilities, and extensive agency reviews; the reports said more about the status of the programme than about the science of acid pollution, and included no policy recommendations. Agency officials doubted that they would be able to meet their goal of an integrated assessment by 1990 estimating the costs and benefits of pollution control options. Dr Laurence Kulp, executive director of NAPAP, put it differently: he argued that the interim report had been delayed because of the rapid accumulation of scientific data.[37]

NAPAP finally issued an interim report in September 1987, and argued that acid rain did not pose an increased threat to lakes, forests or crops.[38] It noted that the Adirondacks had suffered acidification in 10% of its lakes, but argued that there was unlikely to be further damage at projected future levels of pollution. (It assumed that older coal-fired power stations would be retired after fifty years of service, that those continuing in service would be fitted with scrubbers, and that there would be increased reliance on nuclear power – an implausible assumption given all the opposition to nuclear power in the country.)

Although rain was noticeably acidic in many parts of the country, the report continued, there had been few short-term effects on crops or healthy forests, except in acid fog or ozone conditions. SO_2 reductions would not lead to a linear reduction in the acidity of rain.

The report was immediately criticized by the Canadian environment minister, Tom McMillan, and a number of environmental scientists in the United States.[39] Michael Oppenheimer of the EDF called the conclusion that acid rain contributed little to forest damage a "startling misrepresentation". Richard Ayres, a senior attorney with the Natural Resources Defense Council, argued that the report was "designed to make people believe the Reagan administration line that acid rain is not a serious problem. The whole report is political propaganda, not science".[40]

Meanwhile, there had been several attempts in Congress to fight the Reagan administration and enforce effective measures against pollutive emissions. In September 1984 alone, there were at least sixteen bills or amendments on acid pollution before Congress (seven in the Senate, nine in the House of Representatives).[41] Among these was the Waxman-Sikorski Bill (introduced by Representatives Henry Waxman and Gerry Sikorski), which sought a 10 million tonne reduction in SO_2 emissions by 1993. The bill required controls on the fifty most polluting power stations, eight of them in Ohio, seven in Indiana, five each in Missouri and Tennessee, and four each in Illinois, Kentucky, Pennsylvania and West Virginia. The bill's main feature was a fund financed by a surcharge of 0.1 of a cent per kilowatt-hour on all non-nuclear generated electricity in the forty-eight mainland states. This would help pay for retrofitting the fifty power stations with scrubbers. The bill had over 100 co-sponsors in the House, and had strong political support, but was defeated in sub-committee by only one vote.

Individual states were also active opponents of Reagan policy. In March 1984, six north-eastern states (New York, Connecticut, Maine, Vermont, Rhode Island and Massachusetts) filed a suit against the federal government (in effect the EPA) alleging failure to curb acid pollution. The suit charged that the EPA had "ignored sections of the Clean Air Act under which states in the Middle West could be forced to reduce sulphur dioxide emissions",[42] and that inaction by the EPA on acid pollution was resulting in contaminated drinking water supplies, irreversible environmental damage and continued danger to public health. It sought a court order requiring the EPA to "notify offending states, mainly in the Middle West, to cut their sulphur and nitrogen emissions".[43] A similar suit was filed in April 1987, becoming the fifth suit charging the federal government with violations of the Clean Air Act. Others charged the EPA with failing to curb air pollution crossing state boundaries and failing to curb the use of tall smokestacks.

In 1984, New York state – which had tried to take a lead in attempts to promote national pollution controls – launched a $4.3 million project aimed at drawing up the most detailed picture yet of the acidification of ponds and lakes in the Adirondacks, and passed the first law designed specifically to curb acid pollution. The law called for a 12% reduction in SO_2 emissions by 1988 and a 30% reduction by 1991. About one-third of the deposition in New York state is attributable to emissions within the state, but the environmental lobby hoped that the law would act as an example to other states, and ultimately to Congress. New York business groups were opposed to the law, arguing that it would increase electricity bills by up to 9%.

Why, then, was so little achieved during the Reagan administration, despite evidence of acid damage and pressure from Canada? There were a number of reasons. First, President Reagan won office on the most conservative platform in half a century, pledged to reducing government involvement in industry and in people's lives, and to promoting economic recovery. He believed in extensive use of cost-benefit analysis, reliance on the free market to allocate resources as much as possible, and "environmental federalism" – that is, shifting responsibilities for environmental protection to state and local governments. Clearly, this would favour private interests, reduce the role of the federal government in controlling pollution,[44] and emphasize individual state priorities at the expense of national policy.

Reagan also believed that public lands in the west should be opened up for oil and gas exploitation, and that utilities should not be burdened with the extra cost of controlling pollution. He was actively opposed to regulation and taxation – even, apparently, at the cost of amassing the largest national budget deficit in American history. He felt controls would impose costs on utilities and consumers on the basis of insufficient scientific evidence.

Second, public policy in the United States tends either to impose uniform national standards or to allow individual states to go their own way. This means the interests of states are often set off against each other at the cost of national or foreign interests. This is exacerbated by the parochialism of many members of Congress, who tend to put local interests above national interests in order to keep the support of their constituents. Acid pollution is a regional and sectoral problem, so the imposition of uniform national standards would benefit some regions and industries at the cost of others.

The coal industry, the electricity utilities, and coal-producing and electricity-generating states clearly have vested interests in blocking acid pollution control. Like some of its European equivalents, the electricity industry claims that prices would rise dramatically if the industry were forced to invest in flue-gas desulphurization (FGD) or other techniques to clean either the fuel or the gases. Western members of Congress are now becoming aware of the need for legislation to protect the west, which may help to change the political alliance favouring acid pollution control.

The mid-west, which produces most of the pollution, is opposed to investing in expensive new pollution controls, and accuses the north-east of trying to impose a heavy economic burden on mid-western taxpayers. Most of the high-sulphur coal burned in the mid-west is, meanwhile, mined in eastern states like West Virginia, which already has problems with high unemployment among miners. More jobs would likely be lost if there was more demand for low-sulphur coal produced in the west. One of the most vocal opponents of acid rain controls during the Reagan years was Senator Robert Byrd of West Virginia, Senate majority leader until November 1988. He consistently used his influence as majority leader to block acid rain controls. His successor as majority leader is Senator George Mitchell of Maine, an active proponent of acid rain controls. As the Bush administration took office, environmentalists hoped that a combination of Senator Mitchell and a moderate president finally held out the prospect for real progress on acid pollution during 1989 or 1990.

Third, environmental policy in the United States has been treated in recent years as an aspect of health policy. Hence the control of toxic and nuclear wastes has been given more priority because of the apparently greater threat of these wastes to human health. For the time being, acid rain is seen primarily as a threat to ecosystems.[45] However, a 1987 report prepared by the EPA in an effort to review its priorities suggested that perhaps the Agency was concentrating on the wrong problems. Instead of giving priority to toxic wastes, the report concluded, the Agency should be devoting more time to the problems posing the greatest overall risk to human health, including conventional air pollutants such as sulphur and lead.[46]

Canada: putting its own house in order

In 1986, Canada passed a grim milestone in its history: a century of acid pollution. It had been 100 years since the Canadian Copper Company began the open bed roasting of copper ores in Sudbury, Ontario. By 1900 there were more than eighty such open beds, and by 1916 they were pumping 600,000 tonnes of SO_2 into the air every year. Without tall stacks, the emissions were polluting the immediate vicinity, and local farmers were demanding action to prevent the destruction of their crops. The government response (ignoring the basic cause of the problem) was to declare twelve townships "unfit for cultivation" and settlement.[47]

Canada today is both a major source and a major victim of acid pollution. It emits 3.7 million tonnes of SO_2 annually, making it the sixth largest polluter in the world. About half its sulphur deposition originates from the United States, and about half from within Canada. The industrial heartland of Ontario produces the largest domestic emissions of SO_2 and NO_x, and feels the combined effects of its own emissions plus those from south of the border. The biggest sources of Canadian SO_2 are non-ferrous metal smelters, which account for about 45% (60% in eastern Canada). Much of the ore mined on the Canadian Shield contains a substantial proportion of sulphur (about 8% in the Sudbury basin, for example).

The smelting process applies intense heat to the ore, releasing the suphur as SO_2.

Ontario hosts the biggest single source of SO_2 emissions in the world – the Inco (formerly International Nickel Company) smelter complex at Sudbury (360 km north west of Toronto), which in the early 1980s released nearly 650,000 tonnes of SO_2 per year (or 1,770 tonnes per day). This was actually an improvement on 1969, when it released 4,900 tonnes per day and public pressure finally forced government action. In 1970 Inco was ordered to reduce emissions at Sudbury in stages to reach 85% by 1978, and to build a 380 m (1250 ft) superstack to replace existing smaller chimneys. By 1979 Inco was rightly pointing out that the stack (the highest in the world) "permitted recovery of the Sudbury environment to begin." But, as with most tall stacks, the pollution was simply being dispersed further afield. Inco denied that the stack was contributing to long-distance pollution, and, having reduced its emissions by only 30% since 1970, argued that it was not economically or technologically possible to meet the 85% target. In early 1985, in line with growing federal government determination to reduce Canadian SO_2 emissions, Inco suddenly announced that it planned to halve emissions from Sudbury by 1995, at an estimated cost of Can.\$150–250 million.

Despite its irritation with the US position on acid rain, Canada has been slow in reducing its own emissions. It is the third biggest per capita producer of SO_2 and NO_x in the world. Between 1980 and 1983 (the latest year for which figures are available), it managed only a relatively modest 20% reduction in SO_2, and its NO_x emissions actually grew by 3%. This has been a cause of some embarrassment. In its 1984 report, the Canadian Parliamentary Sub-committee on Acid Rain was critical of the federal government, some provincial governments and private enterprise in Canada: "For those Canadians, including members of this Sub-committee, who have travelled to the United States to argue for more stringent controls on American polluters, Canadian government inaction and/or obstinacy with respect to domestic controls has been, quite frankly, an embarrassment." The Canadian regulatory position was "an anomaly, is environmentally harmful, and causes acute political embarrassment to Canadians in discussion with US legislators and officials".[48] Canada must argue "from a position of moral strength. The moral authority of our argument for emission controls in the United States will increase in direct proportion to the extent to which we reduce similar pollutants in Canada".[49]

The acid pollution control strategy of Ontario Hydro, one of the country's largest, non-private emitters of SO_2 and of large quantities of NO_x, was "imprecise and undependable", noted the report.[50] Ontario Hydro is a Crown Corporation, the largest and most powerful electrical utility in Canada, situated in the industrial heartland. It had "the responsibility to lead the way in [pollution] control, to set an example for other industries to emulate. That it has not done so, but instead has forfeited its leadership role, is at best unworthy and, at worst, irresponsible." Ontario Hydro emits around 600,000 tonnes annually of SO_2 and NO_x. Canadian environmentalists are also only too aware that per capita SO_2 emissions in Canada are twice those of the United States, which has about 100 scrubbers on its coal-fired power stations to Canada's none.

The problem lies mainly in the fact that the federal government does not actually have the authority to control SO_2 and NO_x emissions. The 1971 Clean Air Act addressed only local air pollution, not overall levels of pollution for the whole country. Hence the Canadian government has been restricted to encouraging action from the provincial governments. Plans to reduce emissions have been agreed by only seven provinces. Saskatchewan, Alberta and British Columbia have done nothing. Critics charge that Alberta is more interested in energy development than the environment. An official of the provincial environment department reported that the agreement had no application to Alberta, that sulphate deposition was lower in the province than the national average, and that Alberta's soil was not as sensitive to acid deposition as some others.

The controversy between the United States and Canada has so far centred largely on SO_2 emissions, but Canadians are also aware that nitrogen oxides are a major element and that US exhaust gas standards for motor vehicles are far ahead of its own. In the March 1985 announcement of SO_2 reductions, Canada also announced plans to reduce NO_x and introduce new vehicle emission standards (equivalent to those in the United States), to be effective from 1

September 1987. Unleaded petrol is widely available in Canada, and catalytic converters must now be fitted to all new vehicle models.

Acid damage

In 1980, the Ontario environment ministry reported that 140 acidified lakes in the province were devoid of fish, and that a further 48,500 lakes (a quarter of the total) would not be able to tolerate continuing acid inputs for any extended period.[51] Current estimates suggest that acid pollution causes anything from US $180 million to US $250 million worth of damage every year, and puts at risk agriculture, fishing and tourism over large areas of the country.[52] A 1983 study using data gathered over the period 1974–78 suggested that sulphur had caused bronchitis, pneumonia, asthma and other respiratory illnesses among people in southern Ontario, and could have accounted for as many as forty hospital admissions per day during summer.[53]

The spectacular and well-documented examples of acid pollution in Ontario have tended to divert attention from problems elsewhere, but acid damage is either actual or possible in almost every province. Salmon deaths have been recorded in more than twenty rivers in Nova Scotia.[54] In 1979 a Federal Department of Fisheries scientist found that twelve rivers in Nova Scotia were dead or dying as a result of acidification, and that 40–50% of the salmon in the rivers had died that summer.[55] Further west, Alberta, with its oil and gas production and processing, is a major source of emissions. The development of oil sands in the north-west of the province could give rise to a considerable increase in SO_2 emissions, but the provincial government has shown little interest in action to curb pollution. British Columbia, meanwhile, faces a possible threat of emissions from the north-west United States, but its most immediate problem is NO_x. Vancouver is the only major city in Canada with an appreciable NO_x problem, in part because of the NO_x blown north along the coast from US cities to the south.

Other than Ontario, the province most obviously afflicted by acid pollution problems is Quebec. The province has the largest area of land susceptible to acid pollution of any Canadian province, but few studies have yet looked into its effects. Quebec is a major emission producer, thanks particularly to the Noranda Mines smelter at Rouyn-Noranda, which, second only to Inco, annually emits 451,000 tonnes of SO_2. A 1978 study by the provincial environment ministry found the average pH of rainfall in the Rouyn-Noranda area to be just under 4.0. In February 1984, the Quebec provincial government enacted regulations under which industry must reduce its annual SO_2 emissions of one million tonnes by 45% by 1990. Fines as high as US $100,000 could be imposed for failure to comply. In July 1984, following direct federal government pressure, Noranda was ordered to set about reducing emissions from the smelter by 50% (on 1980 emissions of 552,000 tonnes) by 1989. The total cost was estimated at $90 million.

Recent studies have also given rise to concern for Quebec's maple forests. In the early 1980s, there were reports from the southern Quebec counties of Beauce, Megantic, Frontenac and Arthabaska – where maple sugar production has been a major economic activity for centuries – of widespread maple tree dieback and closures of sugar-producing companies. An aerial survey carried out in 1984 by the provincial Ministère de l'Energie et des Ressources confirmed that isolated patches of dying maples were sprinkled throughout southern Quebec. For a province that supplies 75% of the world's maple syrup – and 90% of Canada's – the news was alarming. Ian MacLachlan, a senior official of the Ontario Maple Syrup Producer's Association, is clear about the cause: acid pollution. "Ever since [the Inco superstack at Sudbury] went up," he argues, "you can see the dust around here. People have to wipe it off their cars in the morning".[56]

Following an increase in the number of reports and requests for information about maple dieback, the Ontario Ministry of the Environment (OME) in July 1984 launched an acid pollution research programme to investigate claims that acid pollution was the first link in a process that made maples more susceptible to the effects of extreme weather, insect invasions and fungal diseases. One OME official suggested that a direct cause-and-effect relationship between acid pollution and maple decline would never be proven, and that it "may be the cause in a few trees, it may be exacerbating the situation in other trees, it may be killing off trees in some areas; and in other places, it won't have any bearing at all".[57] He also warned that in ten years, Canadian forests could be as devastated as West German forests were then, unless urgent action was taken.

Bilateral problems, bilateral controls

In his first foreign journey as president, George Bush went to Canada in February 1989 for a meeting with Brian Mulroney. During five hours of talks, acid rain was once again at the top of the agenda. Almost a decade of pressure from the Canadians had not convinced the Americans of the need to control their cross-border SO_2 and NO_x emissions. Several times during the 1980s, the language of diplomacy had barely concealed Canada's growing annoyance at US intransigence. The low point came in February 1984, when the Canadian government delivered a note of protest to the United States, expressing its "deep disappointment" that US plans for the forseeable future failed to include any action to reduce SO_2 emissions. Canada regarded this delay as "an unacceptable breach" of US commitments not to degrade the Canadian environment. It also pointed out that the US decision to limit its efforts solely to more research was a "serious step backward", one that was inconsistent with ministerial level discussions between the two countries; that it failed to "take account of US undertakings contained in the Memorandum of Intent" (see below), and was contrary to assurances given by President Reagan in a March 1981 address to the Canadian Parliament.

Paradoxically, the United States and Canada have a long history of bilateral resource agreements, dating back to the 1909 Boundary Waters Treaty. This established the International Joint Commission (IJC) and reached agreement on the regulation of the Great Lakes and boundary waterways. Between 1972 and 1978, the IJC ran studies which showed that much of the pollution affecting the Great Lakes was airborne. Hence the 1978 Great Lakes Water Quality Agreement included sections on the control of air pollutants. A Research Consultation group was set up in 1978 under the auspices of the IJC, and reported in 1979 that the United States sent far more sulphur to Canada than Canada to the United States.[58]

The US Congress also charged the Department of State with beginning negotiations on a joint air quality agreement with Canada, but any Canadian hopes for rapid progress in that direction were dashed in 1980, when the Carter administration announced plans to convert more than 100 oil-fired power stations to coal. Although mindful of the environmental consequences, Carter felt that, against the background of recent global energy crises, the goal of energy self-sufficiency took precedence.[59] Negotiations nevertheless continued, leading in August 1980 to the signing of a Memorandum of Intent (MOI) Concerning Transboundary Air Pollution. This committed both governments to developing a bilateral agreement and taking interim measures to control transboundary air pollution.

Hopes for progress were again high but negotiations had broken down by the summer of 1982. Reagan administration appointees in the Interior Department and the EPA disagreed with their Canadian counterparts over the degree of the problem, leading Canadian Environment Minister John Roberts to charge that the United States was not living up to the MOI. Canada proposed SO_2 reductions of 50% by 1990, but the United States could agree only to more research; deregulation took priority over solving the acid rain problem.[60] Thereafter, relations on the issue were frosty; Canadian bitterness increased with American indifference. Environment Canada (the federal environment agency) and Canadian NGOs had open political backing from the government in demanding effective measures against acid rain. As early as 1982, an estimated 77% of Canadians saw acid rain as their most serious and pressing environmental problem.[61]

The essential issues in the debate, from Canada's point of view, are that Canada receives more SO_2 from the United States than goes the other way; that more environmental damage has been established in north-eastern Canada than in the north-eastern United States, and that Canada is pushing hard for action (bilaterally and internationally), while the United States is reluctant to cut emissions. In its second report in 1984, the Canadian Parliamentary Sub-committee on Acid Rain observed that the failure of attempts to reach an agreement with the United States on acid rain control was "due principally to the intransigence of the Reagan administration" and had been a bitter setback for Canadians.

It is quite clear that the majority of our American colleagues lack the political will to tackle the problem; indeed, it has been argued by some that the essential problem with the Reagan administration, and with certain members of Congress of both parties, is an overabundance of political will to resist any rational argument in favour of transboundary atmospheric pollution controls.[62]

The February 1984 note of protest repeated yet again that, because more than half the acid deposition in Canada resulted from SO_2 emissions originating in the United States, unilateral Canadian action could not reduce acidic deposition to levels that would adequately protect the Canadian (and north-eastern US) environment. Complementary emission controls in both countries were "absolutely essential." Damage "resulting from inaction" was already enormous and would grow worse.

A month later, Canadian government officials were quoted as saying that US inaction on acid rain was "one of the biggest irritants in US-Canadian relations".[63] On 6 March, in an announcement clearly timed to coincide with that year's Reagan-Trudeau summit, Canada announced that it would unilaterally halve its domestic SO_2 emissions by 1994 east of the Saskatchewan-Manitoba border, at a cost to the federal government of Can.$300 million. Emissions from non-ferrous smelters were singled out as a major target. Making the announcement, Environment Minister Suzanne Blais-Grenier pointed out that acid pollution was costing Canada Can.$250 million per year, and that fishing, tourism and agriculture were at stake over an area of 2.6 million sq km (1 million sq miles). A sum of Can.$25 million had been immediately earmarked for the development of new and cheaper emission control systems. Blais-Grenier said that Canada "must seek a compatible course of action in the United States."

Upon becoming prime minister in 1984, Brian Mulroney emphasized that Canada's intention was first to put its own house in order, hence the launch eleven days before the March 1985 summit of the programme to halve SO_2 emissions by 1994. At the summit, held in Quebec, Mulroney said that the meeting had broken a three-year deadlock between the two countries, and that they had moved to a common position on acid pollution. Yet the only firm action was the appointment of envoys to examine the problem. This was met with scepticism from environmental groups on both sides of the border. Michael Perley of the Canadian Coalition on Acid Rain observed that it was a "clear message that the United States is not willing to address the problem", and argued that the appointment of the envoys was "clearly an admission of defeat" for Mulroney, because it held no US commitment to reduce emissions.

But there was some progress, in word if not in deed. The envoys confirmed in 1986 that acid pollution was a problem, and President Reagan finally agreed in 1986 that power stations and factories in the United States caused acid pollution. Instead of calling for reduced emissions, however, he announced that the United States would spend $2.5 billion over five years on clean-coal technology. Most of this was to be spent on eventually rebuilding old power plants rather than immediately installing pollution control technology. (In his final budget in 1988, Reagan cut funding for the programme.)

At the March 1987 summit, acid rain was again at the top of the agenda. Mulroney proposed once more that Canada and the United States negotiate a bi-lateral accord on acid rain controls. President Reagan agreed to consider the idea, but few outside his administration were convinced. Perley noted that there had been no mention of a time-table: "There's been an attempt on the political level to placate the Canadian Government," he noted, "but in terms of the substance of the issues, we're looking at a fig leaf".[64] US Representative Henry Waxman observed that the President's remarks "did not bring us any closer to an acid rain control program – the rhetoric is just a little smoother". For Senator George Mitchell, author of one of the bills aimed at national acid rain controls, it seemed that Reagan's offer was intended only "to appease his old friend Brian Mulroney without doing anything substantive".[65] In the event, Ronald Reagan left the White House in January 1989 with his acid rain policy largely intact.

The environment became a prominent issue in the 1988 presidential campaign. At the Republican convention in New Orleans, George Bush spoke of the need to "reduce the harm" done by acid rain. Later in the campaign, he promised a specific, detailed programme to cut "millions of tons of sulphur dioxide emissions by the year 2000",[66] and promised to host a White House conference on global environmental problems, including acid rain. In his February 1989 budget address to Congress, President Bush spoke of the need for "a new attitude about the environment". He gave notice that he wanted a new Clean Air Act, including detailed SO_2 reductions in a given period of time. "The time for study alone has passed", he said, "and the time for action is now." William Reilly, the new administrator of the EPA, had already said during his confirmation hearings that legislation on acid rain would be "first out of the box".[67]

The day after his budget speech, Bush flew to Canada for his first meeting with Prime Minister Mulroney. With acid rain at the top of the agenda, Bush repeated his promise of emission reductions, tried to reassure the Canadians that he would be more aggressive on acid rain than Reagan, and promised to restore funding for the clean-coal programme agreed by Reagan. This was "very measurable progress", said Mulroney. The Canadian press was less easily convinced. Press questions at a briefing session following the talks, reported by the *Washington Post*, clearly indicated the suspicion among Canadian reporters that President Bush had "given Canadians the run-around" and that the United States still failed to understand Canada's sense of urgency over acid rain.[68]

Many of the doubts were finally laid to rest in June 1989 when President Bush – as promised – outlined a strong acid pollution control programme. In a marked diversion from the policies of his predecessor, Bush asked Congress to amend the 1970 Clean Air Act with the goal of cutting US SO_2 emissions by 50% (ten million tonnes) and NO_x by 10% (two million tonnes) by the year 2000. Saying "we will make the 1990s the era of clean air", he left it open to industry to decide the best way of reaching that goal. The first phase (a 25% reduction in SO_2 by 1995) will affect 107 power plants in 18 states. They will be allowed to use tradeable pollution permits (an industry that exceeds permitted levels will be allowed to buy "pollution rights" from a company that goes below permitted levels). NO_x emissions will be reduced through stricter emission controls, greater use of clean-burning alternative fuels, and requiring cities with the worst ozone problems to make annual reductions of 3%.

With the announcement, the deadlock which had blocked every

attempted change to the Clean Air Act since 1977 was broken, and the United States finally joined the rest of the industrialized world in agreeing to act on acid pollution.

NOTES

1. *Toronto Globe and Mail*, 15 March 1985.
2. Rhodes, Steven L., "Superfunding acid rain controls – who will bear the costs?", in *Environment* 26:5, July/August 1984.
3. Eckholm, Erik, *Down to Earth* (London: Pluto Press, 1982).
4. National Academy of Sciences, *Atmosphere-Biosphere Interactions: Toward a Better Understanding of the Ecological Consequences of Fossil Fuel Combustion* (Washington, DC: NAS, 1981).
5. Eckholm, see note 3.
6. *New York Times*, 26 March 1987.
7. *New York Times*, 21 February 1989.
8. *New York Times*, 26 February 1984.
9. Vogelmann, H.W., "Catastrophe at Camel's Hump", in *Natural History*, November 1982.
10. Loucks, Dr Orie, Holcombe Research Institute, Butler University, Indianapolis, quoted by Philip Shabecoff, "Damage to trees reported severe", in *New York Times*, 15 April 1984.
11. Gould, Roy, *Going Sour: Science and Politics of Acid Rain* (Boston: Birkhaüser, 1985).
12. *New York Times* 9 November 1988.
13. Agle, Elizabeth C., remarks to Southern States Energy Board Conference on Acid Rain, 18 October 1984.
14. National Clean Air Coalition, Washington, DC.
15. Baes, C.F., and S.B. McLaughlin, "Trace elements in tree rings: evidence of recent and historical air pollution", in *Science* 224, 1984, pp. 834–5.
16. Brezonik, P.L., E.S. Edgerton and C.D. Hendry, "Acid precipitation and sulfate deposition in Florida", in *Science*, 30 May 1980.
17. Yuhnke, Robert E. and Michael Oppenheimer, *Safeguarding Acid-sensitive Waters in the Intermountain West* (Boulder, Colorado: Environmental Defense Fund, 1984).
18. See note 17.
19. Aplet, J.A., M.C. Shikiya, J. Broadbent and E. Nelson, *Acid Deposition in the South Coast Air Basin* (draft). El Monte, California: California Air Resources Board, South Coast Air Quality Management District, June 1984.
20. *New Scientist*, 9 February 1984.

21. World Resources Institute, *The American West's Acid Rain Test* (Washington, DC: WRI Research Report No. 1, March 1985).
22. *New York Times*, 21 February 1989.
23. UNECE figures, reproduced in *The Economist*, 18 February 1989.
24. *New York Times*, 30 August 1988.
25. Regens, James L. and Robert W. Rycroft, *The Acid Rain Controversy* (Pittsburgh: University of Pittsburgh Press, 1988).
26. General Accounting Office, *Acid Rain: Delays and Management Changes in the Federal Research Program* (Washington, DC: GAO, April 1987).
27. Regens and Rycroft, see note 25.
28. National Academy of Sciences, *Acid Deposition: Atmospheric Processes in Eastern North America* (Washington, DC: National Academy Press, 1983).
29. Nierenberg, William A. and others, *Report of the Acid Rain Peer Review Panel* (Washington, DC: Office of Science and Technology Policy, 1983).
30. *National Journal*, 11 May 1985.
31. Conservation Foundation, *State of the Environment 1982* (Washington, DC: Conservation Foundation, 1982).
32. Rosenbaum, Walter A. *Environmental Politics and Policy* (Washington, DC: CQ Press, 1985).
33. O'Donnell, F., "Acid rain controls – is there a 'sensible' compromise", in *Sierra*, November/December 1983.
34. See note 33.
35. *New Scientist*, 9 February 1984.
36. General Accounting Office, see note 26.
37. *New York Times*, 18 September 1987.
38. *New York Times*, 18 September 1987.
39. Joyce, Christopher, "Tress and lakes 'need fear no acid'", in *New Scientist*, 24 September 1987, p. 21.
40. *New York Times*, 18 September 1987.
41. National Clean Air Coalition, Washington, DC.
42. *New York Times*, 21 March 1984.
43. *New York Times*, 3 December 1984.
44. Vig, Norman J. and Michael E. Kraft, "Environmental policies from the seventies to the eighties", in Vig, Norman J. and Michael E. Kraft (eds), *Environmental Policies in the 1980s: Reagan's New Agenda* (Washington, DC: CQ Press, 1984).
45. Schmandt, Jurgen and Hilliard Roderick, *Acid Rain and Friendly Neighbors: The Policy Dispute Between Canada and the United States* (Durham: Duke University Press, 1985).

46. *New York Times*, 19 February 1987.
47. Weller, Phil, *Acid Rain: The Silent Crisis* (Kitchener Ontario: Between The Lines, 1980).
48. O'Donnell, see note 33.
49. House of Commons (Canada), *Time Lost: A Demand for Action on Acid Rain*, Report by the Sub-committee on Acid Rain, Ottawa, 1984.
50. See note 49.
51. Legislature of the Province of Ontario Standing Committee on Resource Development, Final Report, October 1979.
52. *International Herald Tribune*, 8 March 1985.
53. Bates, D.V and R. Sizto, "Relationship between air pollutant levels and hospital admissions in southern Ontario", in *Canadian Journal of Public Health*, 74, March/April 1983.
54. *Acid Rain* (Ottawa: Department of Fisheries and Oceans, 1982).
55. *Montreal Gazette*, 19 September 1979.
56. Norton, Philip, "Decline and fall: something is killing Canada's maple forests", in *Harrowsmith*, 60, April/May 1985.
57. See note 56.
58. Johnson, Janet B., "The dynamics of acid rain policy in the United States", in Ingram, Helen M. and R. Kenneth Godwin (eds), *Public Policy and the Natural Environment* (Greenwich, Conn: JAI Press Inc 1985).
59. Schmandt and Roderick, see note 45.
60. See note 45.
61. Roberts, John, "Acid Rain: A Serious Bilateral Issue". Address to the Air Pollution Control Association, Department of External Affairs, Canada, 31 June 1982.
62. House of Commons (Canada), see note 49.
63. *Toronto Globe and Mail*, 20 March 1984.
64. *New York Times*, 7 April 1987.
65. *New York Times*, 8 April 1987.
66. *New York Times*, editorial, 1 September 1988.
67. *New York Times*, 1 September 1988.
68. *Washington Post*, 11 February 1989.

8. The Soviet Union and Eastern Europe – Socialism and Pollution

It was one of those nasty autumn days when you wake up with a dull headache [said Eduard Vacek, an electrical engineer from Teplice in Czechoslovakia]. A quick glance through the window tells you the dark blanket, suspended over the town for more than a week, has not lifted. Out again into that muck. You think, God, what a stench! What have they been releasing into the air now? They're waging a chemical war against their own people![1]

Marxists often dismiss environmental problems as capitalist problems. Engels wrote in 1876 that capitalists engage in production and exchange for the sake of profit, with no thought for the environmental effects.[2] Socialist economists regularly argue that pollution is a prime example of a social cost incurred through private enterprise, and use it to demonstrate the incompatibility of social welfare and private enterprise under capitalism.[3] By contrast, socialist economic development is portrayed as positive and public-spirited. For instance, Article 18 of the Soviet Constitution states that, in the interests of present and future generations, the necessary steps should be taken "to protect and make scientific, rational use of the land and its mineral and water resources" and "to preserve the purity of air and water. . .and improve the human environment".

Despite the theory, environmental degradation in the Eastern bloc is not only common, but in many places also critically serious. Chernobyl has become a watchword for the failure of Soviet planning. Less well known is the severe pollution in the industrial centres of Poland and Czechoslovakia, and the mounting evidence of damage in East Germany and the Soviet Union. East Germany and Czechoslovakia have the highest per capita emissions of SO_2 in the

Table 8.1: SO$_2$ emissions in the Eastern bloc (in thousand tonnes)

		Most recent figure				% change since 1980	Projected changes
	1980	1983	1984	1985	1986		
USSR	12 800			11 100		−13	−30% (1993)
Poland	4 100			4 300		+5	+20% (1990)
E Germany	4 000	4 000				0	–
Czecho-slovakia	3 100				3 050	−2	−31% (1995)
Hungary	1 633			1 420		−13	−30% (1995)
Yugoslavia	1 175		1 800			+53	–
Bulgaria†	1 034	1 140				+10	–
Romania	200					–	–

† = estimate

Source: United Nations, *National Strategies and Policies for Air Pollution Abatement* (New York: United Nations, 1987).

world. As much SO$_2$ is produced for one East German as for four Britons, eleven Austrians or twenty-three Swiss. Pollution damage is compounded by the concentration of heavy industry in a relatively compact and crowded landmass; a heavy reliance on high-sulphur coal; prevailing winds which blow the pollution across complex river systems and heavily forested regions (and from eastern Europe into the Soviet Union); the inefficiency of many industrial processes, and economic mismanagement. Perhaps nowhere is air pollution more visible, more ugly, or more damaging than in the "black triangle": an industrial and coal-producing area bordered by Leipzig in East Germany, Prague in Czechoslovakia, and Katowice in Poland.

At the same time, progress on controlling SO$_2$ emissions has been much slower in the Eastern bloc than elsewhere. Emissions from the European USSR and Hungary fell by just 13% between 1980 and 1985; in Czechoslovakia and East Germany they remained fairly steady; in Poland, Bulgaria and Yugoslavia, meanwhile, emissions have been growing. Estimates of future trends in the Soviet Union – and, by extension, in the rest of the Eastern bloc – have been thrown into further uncertainty since 1985 by the policies of Mikhail Gorbachev. Glasnost and perestroika, if they survive, not only suggest that much more will be learned about the extent of pollution in the next few years, but also that much more will be done to curb that pollution. In foreign policy addresses, Gorbachev has called for greater co-operation in dealing with global environmental problems. Leonid Brezhnev said much the same but the difference now is that Gorbachev might actually *do* something to put words into action.

The Soviet Union: the world's biggest polluter

The Soviet Union is the world's biggest producer of SO_2. The United Nations published an annual emission figure of 11.1 million tonnes in 1985, but this was only the total for the European part; the national figure is closer to 25.5 million tonnes. About half those emissions (and 40% of NO_x emissions) come from the thermal power plants that generate 60% of Soviet electricity. In addition to domestic pollution, the Soviet Union is also assailed by SO_2 brought on south-westerly winds from Poland, East Germany, Czechoslovakia and Hungary. It receives an estimated five to ten times more pollutants than it sends out over its western borders. In 1979–81 alone, more than 5 million tonnes of sulphur compounds per year were carried into the Soviet Union across its western borders.[4]

Data on environmental deterioration of any kind in the Soviet Union are variable, and Western assessments of Soviet acid pollution have to date had to rely largely on balancing official and unofficial reports. The Soviet delegation to the 1984 Munich conference admitted that there was acid damage in the Soviet Union, the pollution originating both from internal and external sources.[5] But there is much less certainty about the degree of the damage. The critical region is European Russia (west of the Urals), which constitutes less than a quarter of the area of the country, but supports more than three-quarters of the population and most of the industry, agriculture and forestry. About 16% of the European part

(900,000 sq km/350,000 sq miles) is now thought to be affected by acid precipitation, particularly along the western border.

Two marked trends have been identified in forests in the region: the reduced ability of conifers to renew their growth, and a die-off in oaks.[6] In Byelorussia, between 1956 and 1978, the proportion of oak in forests fell from 4.8% to 3.9%, despite the cultivation of 50,000 hectares (125,000 acres) of new oaks. *Pravda* reported in 1984 that vast areas of forest were dying from air pollution near the automobile-manufacturing city of Togliatti, close to Kuibyshev in the Urals.[7] The report observed that forests along the Volga river could also be damaged as a result of the pollution.

Lakes in the European Soviet Union are apparently as susceptible to acidification as lakes in Scandinavia. This applies especially to lakes in the north-western part (such as the Kola Peninsula and Karelia), which are geologically similar to Scandinavia. But no survey of vulnerable lakes has been reported, although low pH values in precipitation have been registered. Soviet acid pollution has particularly serious implications for agriculture. There is an uneven struggle between production and demand, and for years a major policy goal has been to increase grain yields to support increased production of meat and other livestock products. But grain production frequently falls short of demands, obliging the Soviet Union to rely on imports.

Drought, poor organization, poor transport and distribution systems, waste, inefficiency, bad discipline, and inadequate maintenance of machines and other equipment all contribute to the failure to meet agricultural goals. But the Soviet Union now seems to be facing the prospect of additional shortages caused by acid damage. Acid pollution is believed to be implicated in the annual loss of millions of roubles worth of agricultural yields. Some 15% of the harvest in an area of 40 million hectares (100 million acres) had been lost by 1984, representing yields worth $580 million.[8]

In 1978, *The Destruction of Nature in the Soviet Union* was published in the United Kingdom. The book, written by "Boris Komarov" (said to be the pseudonym for a senior Soviet official), argued that ecological damage in the Soviet Union was primarily a result of the self-interested actions of a bureaucratic elite. This elite knew the scale of the Soviet ecological crisis, but had neither the desire nor the means to resolve it because to do so would threaten their privileges. 'Komarov' noted that the Soviet Union had the strongest emission standards in the world for many pollutants, but that they generally remained "an abstraction, an ideal for which industry should strive". Dust and particle filters had been fitted to many factory chimneys, he noted, which gave the visual appearance of clean air; but SO_2 and other gas emissions remain.[9]

Electrification has been a central energy goal in the Soviet Union since the revolution, prompted by massive domestic energy resources. These include the biggest coal reserves in the world (mined in the Ukraine, Siberia, and Kazakhstan), major oil fields in the Caspian Sea and Black Sea, and natural gas fields in the Caspian and in the Urals. Oil and natural gas is taken in huge pipelines from the Volga and Caspian fields to the major industrial centres of the Soviet Union and Eastern Europe. Between 1980 and 1985, the Soviets reduced their reliance on fossil fuels from 81% to 70% of energy needs; by 1990, the proportion is projected to have fallen to 50%.[10] Under the State Energy Programme, designed to take energy planning well into the 1990s, the Soviet Union has promoted a substitution of oil by natural gas; increased use of secondary energy resources (such as waste heat from industry); accelerated development of coal-burning power plants using low-sulphur coals from the eastern part of the country, and the development of hydro-, geo-thermal and nuclear power, which between them should supply half of Soviet energy needs by the early 1990s.

As for reducing SO_2 and NO_x, the Soviets see domestic emissions as less of an issue than the so-called "trans-boundary fluxes" affecting neighbouring countries. The Soviet Union argues that only 3–4% of the air pollutants produced within the country ever cross Soviet borders, and so is unwilling to commit itself to any total reductions by a fixed percentage. It claims instead that it need only reduce its transboundary fluxes by 30% in order to fulfil international demands and show consideration for the environment of other countries. Hence its accession to the 30% Club and its plan to reduce those fluxes by 30% by 1995.

A 2 million tonne cut in SO_2 emissions in 1980–84 was achieved by using fuel desulphurization, flue gas desulphurization, new low-waste and low-energy technologies, energy conservation, extensive use of low-sulphur coals and gas, and the development of nuclear and hydro-power.[11] These reductions were intended to have the biggest impact in the European Soviet Union. The Soviet Union plans to further reduce its SO_2 emissions by using low-sulphur coal and replacing its fossil fuel-fired power stations with nuclear power plants, apparently despite Chernobyl. There are also plans to control NO_x emissions from industry and power plants by modifying combustion processes.

Given the Soviet Union's extensive public transport system and the lack of private vehicles, NO_x from road traffic is not a major issue. Trucks are the source of more than 70% of the exhaust gases from Soviet motor vehicles. Future measures are aimed at designing new types of engines, using more diesel engines, and increasing the production of vehicles operating on compressed or liquefied natural gas, gasohol or electricity. More new cars will also be fitted with catalytic converters. According to Soviet calculations, these measures will reduce emissions from motor vehicles by 30% by 1993, even while the number of vehicles on Soviet roads increases.

The Chernobyl disaster in April 1986 revealed at least three major characteristics of Soviet environmental planning, all of which have serious implications for air pollution policy. First, there is the prevailing secrecy of Soviet society. It was two days before news of Chernobyl was released, and at least a month before the full details emerged. Secrecy of this kind makes it difficult to be certain about the extent of acid pollution damage within the Soviet Union. To this must be added the Soviet reluctance to reduce its total SO_2 emissions. No matter how quickly and fully it meets its 30% Club obligations, reductions in "transboundary fluxes" will amount to a tiny fraction of total emissions. Until the Soviet Union is willing to reduce total emissions, the prospects for acid damage remain serious. In stark contrast to Chernobyl, news about the December 1988 Armenian earthquake was released immediately, and media access in the aftermath was relatively open. Apart from the consequences of glasnost, the Soviets may have been motivated at least in part by the fact that the earthquake was a natural disaster. Except for what it revealed about Soviet building standards, it did not reflect badly on the country's technology, unlike Chernobyl.

Second, there is the Soviet propensity for sacrificing public safety, and – by extension – environmental quality, in the interests of cutting short-term costs. This was emphasized once again in the Armenian earthquake: despite the fact that the area is earthquake-prone, apartment blocks were jerry-built. Western rescue teams sent in to help search for survivors not only commented on the inadequacy of building and public safety standards, but also on the slowness with which public service agencies responded to a national disaster. Against this background, it is difficult to be optimistic about the efficacy of Soviet controls on SO_2 and NO_x emissions.

Third, the Chernobyl disaster was a prime example of what Charles Ziegler calls Soviet technological hubris, or arrogance.[12] While admitting that nuclear power had gone out of control, Gorbachev also rejected suggestions that the accident would slow the Soviet nuclear programme. The programme will apparently proceed as planned. While this may reduce Soviet dependence on fossil fuels, it may simply replace one polluting technology with another.

One source of hope for the future may lie in glasnost and the new ability of Soviet scientists and academics to voice their concerns about the environnent. "I do not think we have yet fully realized the size of the crime we are committing against nature and future generations of inhabitants in our homeland", says Viktor Kazakov, a writer who recently publicized the deteriorating condition of the Caspian. "Facts about the most major ecological losses have been kept secret for decades".[13] Local environmental groups have been springing up, and the media have been openly criticizing polluting industries, even going so far as to name responsible individual administrators. In June 1988, for example, Moscow Radio reported a meeting of the All Russia Nature Protection Society which heard of 3–4% increases in the number of mentally sick and retarded children in the country's most polluted towns, and of air pollution in Moscow, Leningrad and Kemerovo exceeding permitted levels.[14]

Ziegler argues that the development of Soviet environmental law over the last three decades has reflected a growing attentiveness to environmental questions, but, at the same time, a reluctance to take major initiatives in the area. Fears of regional tampering with nationally set production quotas has made central authorities reluctant to delegate significant powers to the governments of the Soviet republics.[15] Any talk of using economic incentives to promote environmental legislation is seen as an unacceptable challenge to the organizational basis of the centrally planned economy. At the same time, Ziegler notes that while Soviet environmental administration is, in theory, highly centralized, it is, in practice, fragmented and unco-ordinated, and lacks any real sense of direction. The Soviet bureaucratic system has an inherent conservatism that discourages tampering. Any changes that might have been attempted by Brezhnev, Andropov or Chernenko were in the nature of fine tuning rather than fundamental reform.

But the essence of Gorbachev's new broom is restructuring, or perestroika. While no country has yet designed an effective and comprehensive administrative and legislative structure for environmental planning, the Soviet Union is further from that goal than most. Much now depends on whether Gorbachev can survive, how far he can change the Soviet system, and whether his changes can really bring higher productivity and greater air pollution control at the same time.

East Germany: highest per capita SO$_2$ emissions on earth

East Germany claims that if it had the money, it would be actively in favour of controls on atmospheric pollution. "Our experts are working on various methods to reduce emissions", commented an East German diplomat at Munich. "But we are in no position to present a time schedule for the exact implementation of all measures. Even though there is indeed a will, the economic constraints are not easily overcome".[16]

All of which is unfortunate, because East Germany is the most heavily industrialized country in the Eastern bloc, and its per capita SO$_2$ emission rates are the highest in the world at 235 kg (518 lbs) per person. This is nearly three times the rate in the Soviet Union, and nearly twenty-three times the rate in Switzerland. Perhaps the single most concentrated source of SO$_2$ in the world is the industrial triangle of Leipzig, Karl-Marx-Stadt (formerly Chemnitz), and Dresden, near the Czech border. Annual East German SO$_2$ missions are thought to be about 4 million tonnes, of which nearly two-thirds is deposited within the country. The rest is sent out to neighbouring countries, mainly Poland,

Czechoslovakia, West Germany, the Soviet Union and Sweden. On the positive side, emission levels have remained fairly constant since the early 1970s, while industrial production has grown by about 80%.

About 90–95% of the SO_2 comes from lignite. East Germany is the world's biggest producer of lignite, accounting for more than a quarter of the world total. Hence lignite accounts for the bulk of East German energy demand (70% in 1980, compared with 18% from oil, 9% from natural gas, and 3% from nuclear power). While the contribution of coal is expected to remain steady, and that of oil and gas to fall, nuclear power capacity is expected to more than double by 1990. About 12% of East Germany's electricity is already generated by nuclear power; one large plant is in operation and three are on order.

With a water content of just over 50% and a carbon content of just under 25%, lignite has a low thermal and energy value, so large quantities must be burned to generate the same amount of energy as lesser quantities of oil. On the other hand, the sulphur content of East German lignite is only about 1–2%, and it contains elements that give it a degree of built-in alkalinity which helps neutralize some of the potential acidity. Its high water content also means that it cannot be burned at high temperatures, so the formation of NO_x is low – about 90% lower than hard coal.

NO_x emissions from East German road vehicles are relatively low. Many vehicle engines are two-stroke, and produce, on average, only a tenth of the NO_x produced by four-stroke engines. Speed limits have been introduced: 100 kph (62 mph) on highways, 80 kph (50 mph) on main roads, and 30–50 kph (20–30 mph) in urban areas. "Transportation optimizing" (encouraging the use of rail and water transport, public transport in the larger cities, and more vehicles powered by natural gas), is regarded as the key to minimizing NO_x emissions from road vehicles.

Data on established and anticipated damage from air pollution in East Germany are variable, reflecting a Soviet-type secrecy. East Germany does not readily admit that forest damage exists, and no precise figures are given officially. However, damage to 350,000 hectares (865,000 acres), or 12% of the total forested area has been reported.[17] About 75% of East German forest is coniferous (spruce and pine), and 25% deciduous (mainly beech). Nearly two-thirds of all forests are owned by the state, 29% by agricultural co-operatives and the remaining 6% by the church and by individuals. The areas most affected by environmental damage correspond with the major mining and industrial centres. Acid damage has been reported in the Dübener Heide and Lausitzer Heide (heaths), in the central highlands, and in the south-west.[18]

Soil acidification has also been confirmed in the Erzegebirge mountains on the Czechoslovak border, and there have been official admissions of forest damage in the industrial areas of Leipzig, Bitterfeld and Halle. Considerable damage is also believed to have occurred around Karl-Marx-Stadt, in the Cottbus area on the Polish border, in the Marienberg and Annaberg on the Czechoslovak border, and in the Fichtelgebirge on the West German border. Visiting Swedish experts noted soil acidification in the south, south-east and south-west of the country, which the East Germans blame on unnatural climatic conditions. No surface water acidification is acknowledged, on the grounds that surface water is often naturally acid (as low as pH 4.9 in highland moors), or that excess acidity is buffered by the soil (in central and northern parts of the country).

The concept of forest damage from air pollution is by no means new to the East Germans. The Tharand Institute, a forest research institute founded in 1811, has carried out research on air pollutants and their influence on trees and other vegetation since the middle of the nineteenth century. Experiments are carried out today in an installation – unique in Eastern Europe – where pure or mixed gases are blown into mobile greenhouses containing conifers, crops or fruit trees. East Germany has also built up a considerable store of knowledge about the effects of air pollution on vegetation, much of which has already been used to counter various types of damage. Research has, for example, been carried out into adapting forests to present and continued high levels of air pollutants. Different conifers, particularly spruce, are being improved by breeding to produce varieties more resistant to pollution.

Management methods for badly affected forest areas are being designed, and research carried out into the effects of mineral fertilizers, to establish whether they can strengthen and revitalize trees. Species of trees best adapted to different sites are selected;

complete stands, or trees in the outer parts of stands, are used as protective screens. Interim protective measures include intensive fertilizing (23,000 hectares/57,000 acres per year), the "spread of risk" (mixed plantations of conifers and deciduous trees so that if one species is knocked out, the other will provide a harvest), and the breeding of species tolerant to polluted air.

Despite all this, East German officials and scientists tend to play down the implications of transboundary air pollution and acidification. Damage in industrial areas is described as a "local problem". While West Germans speak of *saurer Regen* (acid rain), East Germans speak of *rauchgeschädigte Flachen* (areas damaged by smoke). East German authorities hold that forest damage is due to the effect of toxic gaseous pollutants (mainly SO_2 and other airborne pollutants) and the synergistic effect of impaired breathing and nutrient uptake of trees. During extreme climatic situations, such as the droughts of 1975–76 and 1982–83, and the frost of 1978–79, the damage was worse.

East Germany is a member of the 30% Club, and the expansion of nuclear power figures prominently among the several measures being taken, or planned, to reduce emissions and counteract damage.[19] Daily nationwide measurements of SO_2 levels have been made since 1978, and the East Germans say that total emissions will not be allowed to increase even while industrial production continues to expand. Lignite will continue to be the most important source of energy (despite the fact that it will be increasingly expensive to produce, is difficult to mine without contaminating groundwater, and reserves are limited). There have also been calls for energy conservation and more efficient energy use, the installation of district heating systems, and the use of more modern gas heating systems.

The technology for efficient combustion, desulphurization and filtration is still in the experimental stage. Although emission reduction technology has yet to be applied in any full-scale power plants, this may be about to change. Coal gasification and coal liquefaction are being examined as ways of making energy use more efficient. At the same time, East Germany has developed its own simple desulphurization process for lignite: in large plants, crushed coal is mixed with 10% lime before combustion. Desulphurization levels as high as 50–60% have been achieved and improvements are expected.

One experimental plant began operations in 1983, and new plants are thought to be under construction in the vicinity of Leipzig and Karl-Marx-Stadt.

Czechoslovakia: a catalogue of horrors

Describing the state of Czechoslovakia's environment in April 1982, the newspaper *Prace* noted that the term "ecological catastrophe" was not "just a turn of phrase", but a real possibility unless "radical measures" were taken. The country's air pollution problems have moved some Czechoslovak scientists to warn that by the year 2000, parts of the country could be unfit for human habitation.[20] The industrial towns and cities of northern Bohemia in particular are among the most polluted in the world. Yet the government view is that conditions in Czechoslovakia are under control and no more alarming than elsewhere in Central Europe, and that Western Europe is, anyway, the source of two-thirds of Czechoslovakia's SO_2.

In fact, Czechoslovakia is one of the biggest producers of SO_2 in the world, emitting just over 3 million tonnes annually. It has the same population as the Netherlands, but produces ten times the emissions. That puts it second only to East Germany in terms of per capita SO_2 production. The Czechs produce nineteen times as much SO_2 per head of population as the Swiss, and three times as much as the British. Between 1980 and 1986, Czech SO_2 emissions were reduced by just 2%, but Czechoslovakia is a member of the 30% Club, and has committed itself to a 31% reduction by 1995. This is to be achieved by fitting scrubbers to power stations and relying more on nuclear power.

The announcement of Czechoslovakia's accession in September 1984 contrasted sharply with the claim of the Czech delegation at Munich three months before. They had said that it would be impossible to cut emissions, and that they could only try not to increase emissions. It also contrasted with the doubts expressed by a Czech government delegation during a visit to Sweden in May about whether reductions of 30% were physically possible for any country. The sudden change of policy may have been the result of pressure on Czechoslovakia from its neighbours, particularly the Soviet Union, which receives much of Czechoslovakia's SO_2.

In December 1983, the Czechoslovak human rights group Charter 77 copied and released in the West a confidential report prepared by the Czechoslovak Academy of Sciences (CSAV).[21] The report, intended for circulation only to senior government and Communist Party officials, revealed that Czechoslovak economic policy is to increase industrial production and expand energy supply, while cutting environmental management budgets. According to Charter 77, expenditure on environmental protection was cut from 1.3% of total investments in the 1976–80 five-year plan to 0.85% in the 1981–85 plan. The government denied this, saying that investments had gone up by 30%. Charter 77 pointed out that about $225 million was budgeted to be spent in the period 1981–85 on measures to avert environmental damage, while the estimated annual cost of damage was closer to $1.25–1.5 billion.

Charter 77 said the government was witholding vital information. The government replied that there was an open and active public debate on environmental issues. There is an element of truth in both views, because the Czechoslovak press (unlike its Soviet equivalent, until recently at least) is allowed to be openly critical of environmental conditions in the country. But public debate has so far failed to improve Czechoslovakia's dire environmental conditions. According to the Academy of Sciences report, 20–25% of all Czechs are suffering directly from the adverse effects of high ambient SO_2 levels.

As with East Germany, the crux of the problem is Czechoslovakia's dependence on lignite, which heats homes, produces electricity, and fuels industry. Czechoslovakia uses about 60–80 million tonnes of lignite per year. The best coal is now believed to have been used up; what is left is of less calorific value, with a high sulphur and ash content. To generate the same amount of energy, larger quantities of this coal must be mined and used. With domestic and industrial energy demands constantly rising, coal is unlikely to lose its economic grip over Czechoslovakia in the short term.

Czechoslovakia has two major regions: the Czech Lands and Slovakia. The Czech Lands (particularly Bohemia) is where about 80% of the country's lignite is mined. It is the most heavily industrialized and the most heavily polluted part of the country. This heavy dependence on lignite produces an average rainfall pH of 3.5.

Prague itself, by government admission, is "a disaster zone", with SO_2 emissions often twenty times above permitted limits.[22] But the region pin-pointed by the CSAV report as by far the worst affected in the country is northern Bohemia, in and around the city of Most. Six northern Bohemian power stations alone produce 60% of Czechoslovakia's electricity,[23] and account for nearly three-quarters of Czech SO_2 emissions. The stations burn huge quantities of low-calorie lignite, mined from extensive local opencast pits, which give the region its local nickname of "the lunar country". To clear the way for mining, twenty northern Bohemian villages sitting on top of lignite deposits were pulled down, and the older parts of Most were moved to give access to the coal beneath the city. One of the largest surface mines, at the foot of the Erzegebirge, is 100 km long and 20 km wide (62 miles by 12 miles).

According to the CSAV report, infant mortality in 1980 in northern Bohemia was 12% higher than the national average, and the occurrence of respiratory diseases was 120% higher than the Czech Lands' average. Children in parts of Bohemia have 20% more red blood cells and slower bone growth than the national average, and leukaemia is more prevalent. In the Most region, only 38% of adolescents were free of illness, a record worse even than that of the Czech Lands as a whole (57.7%). Particularly common were infections of the respiratory tract, of the skin and subcutaneous tissues, and ailments affecting muscles, bone and ligaments. The average life span for northern Bohemia as a whole was three to four years shorter than the national average. Doctors and pharmacists have been leaving the region at rates high enough to merit comment in the Czech Communist Party newspaper.[24]

Local and national authorities are not unaware of conditions in the area. In fact, local residents are given special privileges. The miners have the highest salaries in Czechoslovakia (dismissed by cynics as "burial money"), the best supplied shops and shorter waiting times for apartments and cars. They are allowed longer holidays abroad and receive a bonus for each year of their "loyalty". Children are sent on special holidays abroad or to less polluted regions within the country. Special "smog drills" have also been instituted in the Most region. Implemented twenty-four hours after SO_2 levels have exceeded prescribed limits, factories and power stations are required to switch to special reserves of high-quality coal, schools are forbidden to allow children outdoors, extra vitamins are handed out in hospitals, and outdoor sports competitions are cancelled.[25]

The 1987 EMEP report on Europe's forests found that about half the forests in Czechoslovakia were acid-damaged.[26] With about a third of its land area under forest, timber is a major economic resource for Czechoslovakia, so acid pollution poses considerable economic problems. The stages in forest dieback are similar to those in other Central European countries: twenty years ago individual spruces died and the crowns of older trees began thinning; fifteen years ago groups of trees died and forest mushrooms and berries disappeared; ten years ago the forests died over large, contiguous elevated areas; now the damage is spreading to valleys. Deciduous trees are also dying. The CSAV report predicted future shortages of timber in the country, and predicted that half of all the woodland in Czechoslovakia would be damaged by the end of the century if present trends continued.

Current Czechoslovak forestry policy is to replace conifers with more acid-resilient deciduous trees; among other things, pointed spruces are being imported from Canada. In highland areas, dead forest is apparently being clear-felled (for timber, and possibly also to prevent the spread of insects and fungi) in "corridors" tens of kilometres wide. But this has had the effect of allowing air pollutants free passage to forests further down the mountainsides, and brings the added danger of flooding after the spring snowmelt.

Water pollution has also long been a major problem in Czechoslovakia. An increase in the use of artificial fertilizers since 1979 and the dumping of sewage into public waterways has been compounded by fall-out from industrial emissions. Waste water from cities and industries is allowed to flow into rivers without purification or adequate treatment. The lack of foreign currency prevents the importation of equipment for treatment plants.[27] The burning of large quantities of lignite, without flue gas treatment, poses the added danger of acidification and heavy metal contamination.

Contamination of milk is a major cause of milk shortages, and the lack of legal requirements to monitor chemical contamination of food is one reason why few countries will import Czechoslovakian meat. A West German team visiting Czechoslovakia in 1984 reported that in the most acidified areas of the country, water from shallow wells could no longer be used as drinking water. Children and pregnant women are advised to move to other regions. Bratislava is said to be short of drinking water and doctors advise mothers to give their children mineral water to drink. The CSAV report pointed out that practically all mountain lakes were acidified, and even lowland lakes, which have better natural buffering capacity, were endangered.

Like the Soviets, the Czechs plan to expand their nuclear power industry, but – again like the Soviets – the Czechoslovak nuclear power industry has been plagued by faults and mishaps, many of which Charter 77 ascribes to operator errors. Unlike most other nuclear countries, Czechoslovakia apparently has few qualms about siting its reactors close to people – all are within 10 km (6 miles) of human settlements. At the Munich conference, the Czechoslovak delegation claimed that the government had adopted new restrictions for industry; made changes in energy policy aimed at "rationalizing" energy consumption; increased the import of Soviet natural gas; lowered the sulphur content of coal and oil; invested in extensive development of desulphurization techniques (including the launch of a joint project with the Soviet Union for the construction of a desulphurization plant); and was accelerating the construction of nuclear power and heating plants. The Czechoslovak government was aware of the acid pollution problem, said the delegation, but was also aware that "without effective measures in other states" there was no real prospect of improvement.[28]

But that was 1984. In 1987, President Gustav Husak announced a doubling of investment in environmental protection during the eighth 5-year-plan, to nearly $200 million. Much of this is to go towards installing SO_2 scrubbers imported from the Soviet Union. A test scrubber has been fitted to a power station in Bohemia; if it works, the system will be expanded. The expansion of nuclear power meanwhile continues apace, with the object of closing down all northern Bohemia's fossil fuel-powered stations by 2020.[29] This leaves the prospect of at least another 10–20 years of serious acid pollution in the region. Czechoslovakian action on pollution will be too late to improve the quality of life of the next one or two generations of Bohemians, or to save hundreds of thousands of hectares of forest in Czechoslovakia, Poland and East Germany.

Poland: the world's most polluted country?

In a detailed and remarkably frank paper to the 1984 Munich conference, the Polish delegation admitted that SO_2 emissions had become a major problem in Poland. Recommended annual concentrations had been exceeded over 3% of the country, and transboundary emissions were augmenting domestic ones. The paper confirmed reports in the Western press which painted a picture of Poland as one of the world's most polluted countries. The emergence of the independent trade union Solidarity created a new awareness among Poles themselves of "the impending dangers of pollution, ecological destruction and resulting health hazards, [and produced] a complete loss of faith in the belief that scientific and technological expertise and innovation" would always avail.[30]

Hard coal containing 1.8–4% sulphur is the source of most of Poland's environmental problems. About 70% of air pollutants come from industrial sources, 15% each from transport and from district and domestic heating. Poland annually emits about 4.3 million tonnes of SO_2, which is an increase of 5% on 1980. By 1990, emissions are likely to be 4.9 million tonnes, an increase of 20% on 1980. The average annual deposition rate is 14 tonnes per sq km (36 tonnes per sq mile), which is well below the rates in East Germany or Czechoslovakia. But deposition rises dramatically in the heavily industrialized region of Silesia in south-western Poland (part of the "black triangle"), where average deposition is 50 tonnes/sq km/year (130 tonnes/sq mile/year).

Information about worsening conditions existed prior to the emergence of Solidarity, but was largely suppressed or censored.

One 1980 government report, (prepared by a fourteen-member commission from the National Centre for Environmental Protection and Development and the State Environmental Inspectorate), warned that environmental destruction in Poland was about to reach "the proportions of a national crisis".[31] In 1981 Solidarity handed out leaflets warning that:

> The biological basis of our country, our health, our children and future generations continues to be seriously endangered by the devastation of the environment in which we live...One-third of the country's food is poisoned, one-fifth of the population is seriously endangered by air pollution, one-third of Polish rivers are completely dead, the Baltic is dying, while 78% of lakes have levels of pollution that far exceed any acceptable standard.[32]

The Polish Constitution states that Poland will "ensure the protection and rational development of the natural environment, which constitutes both a national resource and part of a common heritage". Since the second world war, a large body of environmental legislation, policy-making machinery, and control and research agencies has been created in Poland. But at the same time, Polish planners have been committed to rapid economic and industrial development. With industry and the economy under state control, Poland thought it could avoid the environmental problems seemingly inherent in Western capitalism.[33] Exactly the opposite has happened. Poland's economic crisis and the world recession tended to push environmental problems off centre-stage in the mid-1980s, so the capital to invest in pollution control was not available.[34] Despite the actual and potential costs of air pollution, the resolution of problems such as the acute shortage of basic consumer goods took precedence.

Poland nevertheless plans an emission control programme from 1991, including FGD, and fluidized bed combustion for high-sulphur coals. But the Poles warned at Munich that it was impossible to expect a significant reduction of total Polish emissions before 1990, the main limitations being "economic, technical and organizational".[35] Poland has neither joined the 30% Club nor ratified the ECE convention. At the second meeting of the Executive Body of the convention in September 1984, the Poles announced that it was economically impossible for Poland to undertake even a 30% reduction of SO_2 emissions until between 1993 and 1995.

Coal (mainly hard coal, with smaller quantities of lignite) provides more than three-quarters of Poland's energy needs, and earns 15% of export revenues. With 180 million tonnes of hard coal mined or excavated each year, Poland is the fourth largest producer in the world (surpassed only by China, the Soviet Union and the United States). Hard coal – called "the black gold" of Poland – has been mined and extracted in Silesia for decades. The Upper Silesian industrial region is the most highly industrialized part of the province of Katowice. This in turn is Poland's largest industrial region, the source of 30% of the nation's wealth. Covering only 2% of Poland's land area, it is home to 10% of the population.

Katowice is also the most polluted region in Poland, accounting for a third of Polish dust and gas emissions. Industries there emit an estimated 600–700,000 tonnes of dust and 1.77 million tonnes of gas (mostly SO_2) each year. The average annual fall-out of dust in Poland is 6 tonnes/sq km/year (15.6 tonnes/sq mile/year). Warsaw receives about 250 tonnes/sq km/year (650 tonnes/sq mile/year) – the maximum permitted level – but Chorzow, in Katowice, has a fall-out of nearly 900 tonnes/sq km (2,350 tonnes/sq mile/year) and Bytom, Gliwice and Zabrze a staggering 1,000 tonnes/sq km (2,600 tonnes/sq mile/year).

Rafal Serafin warns that 70% of Katowice's population lives in conditions harmful to health. He quotes studies in the Szopienice district of Katowice which reveal that 35% of children and adolescents examined had symptoms of lead poisoning, which until only recently had been classified as an "occupational disease". Workers suffer 25% more accidents and illness at work than elsewhere, while the general population suffers 15% more circulatory diseases, 30% more cancers and 47% more respiratory diseases than the rest of the country. In some industries, 80% of the workers end up on disablement pensions. The children may be affected much earlier by the high levels of cadmium (four to six times the admissible level). Half the country's schools for mentally retarded children are situated in Katowice.[36]

One of the biggest sources of pollution was the aluminium smelter at Skawina (southeast of Krakow), closed in 1981 after a campaign led by the Polish Ecology Club (Polski Klub Ekologiczny), an independent environmental pressure group set up in 1980. The smelter began production in 1954, when its annual capacity was projected at 15,000 tonnes. But production steadily increased, reaching 53,000 tonnes in 1980. As it grew, so the plant was extended: old equipment was kept going long after it should have been retired, no improvements were made in the production process, and no anti-pollution measures were taken. Annual emissions totalled 2,500 tonnes, 38% of which was in the form of gas. Westerly winds blew the emissions over the town of Skawina and the south-western part of Krakow. The above average humidity (the annual mean is over 80%) promoted the formation of harmful concentrations of SO_2 and hydrogen fluoride that corroded stone and stucco buildings and weakened walls, roofs and metal elements.

Surface water and groundwater was contaminated by toxic compounds washed by rainfall from waste deposits dumped in the vicinity of the smelter. Fluorine compounds drained the soil of the minerals that would normally neutralize them, causing poor harvests in the area. Toxic substances accumulated in crops destined for livestock fodder, and human health was endangered. Poland's high SO_2 levels now pose a serious health hazard to one in five Poles,[37] and by 1990 more than a quarter of the population could be affected. Not even southern Polish health resorts such as Zakopane, Krynica Gorska, Rabka and Szczawnica – once famed for their reviving and curing air - are immune. SO_2 and other pollutants may be causing or contributing to many avoidable deaths every year.

The city of Krakow was one of the first to be included in the UNESCO list of sites of the world's cultural heritage. Its medieval old town is regarded as one of the finest surviving examples of its kind. The city square – the largest in Europe – remains much as it was in the thirteenth century. But Krakow is only 65 km (40 miles) south-east of Katowice. Emissions from Katowice, added to those from Krakow's own industries, have made it one of the most polluted cities in Europe, subject to frequent acid smogs. Industrial dust levels are nine times the acceptable national limit, and water trucks have to spray the central square and marketplace throughout the day, in an effort to keep the dust down.

To make matters worse, Krakow sits in a humid valley, its climate often holding the effluents in a layer 80–100m (260–330 ft) above the ground. The result is that the city's buildings are corroding, and their walls and roofs are being weakened. Corroded statues on the sixteenth century church of Saints Peter and Paul have been taken away for safekeeping. Even the gold roof of the cathedral chapel at Wawel castle is dissolving. Between 1975 and 1980, a total of $3 million was spent on building renovation. In Katowice itself, acid pollution has so corroded the railway tracks that trains are restricted to travelling at 40 km per hour (25 mph).[38]

Poland has about 8.6 million hectares (21.2 million acres) of forest, covering a quarter of the total land area. About 6% of the forest (500,000 hecatres/1.23 million acres) is thought to be damaged, and trees over an area of 200,000 hectares (50,000 acres) are thought to have died.[39] Most of the forests (about 80%) are coniferous and so susceptible to acidification. Forest damage is worst in the Upper Silesian industrial region, the area around Krakow, and in the Legnica-Glogow basin.

Bad as the position already is, Polish scientists fear that worse is yet to come. The Belchatow Industrial Region, now under construction in central Poland, is expected to be a major new source of pollution. Its power plants will burn locally excavated lignite, and are expected to emit between 900,000 and 1.2 million tonnes of SO_2 per year, or 15% of Poland's total forecast SO_2 emissions for 1990–1995. About 50,000 hectares (125,000 acres) of forest will fall within the highest danger zone for pollution. Polish environmental scientists are predicting evergreen forest losses of up to three million hectares (7.5 million acres) by 1990 – worth $1.5 billion at 1980 prices – if industrialization proceeds as planned.

Soil acidification, affecting arable land and groundwater deposits in turn, is expected to spread. Most Polish soils are naturally acidic podsols and so are susceptible to acidification. Crop damage would add an unwelcome burden to the Polish economy, which is heavily dependent on agriculture. Half the land is ploughland, and more than 30% of the working population are farmers.

About 11% of coal-burning industrial plants in Poland currently have some kind of flue gas treatment equipment, but they are not thought to be very efficient. The bulk of investments in environmental protection are currently put into curbing water pollution. There is no immediate prospect of any substantive measures to curb air pollution until well into the next decade.

Hungary and the rest of Eastern Europe

Hungary, Bulgaria, Romania and Yugoslavia also feel the effects of acid pollution. Bulgaria and Romania are the least industrialized countries in the Eastern bloc, but this has not spared them; an estimated 170,000 hectares (420,000 acres) of Romanian forest have been damaged by acid rain.[40] Forest damage has been reported in Yugoslavia too, but figures are imprecise. One estimate is 450,000 hectares (1.1 million acres) of forest damaged, possibly already dead.[41] An additional 50,000 hectares (125,000 acres) are thought to be seriously affected.

Even official Hungarian publications admit that more than 4 million Hungarian citizens (35–40% of the population) live with "inadmissible levels" of air and water pollution. The amount of traffic on Budapest roads has more than doubled in the past ten years, creating frequent smogs. This has partly offset the benefits of Hungary's programme to convert residential heating from coal to natural gas, now 60% completed. The government has launched a campaign to clean up the environment generally, and has budgeted a generous 2% of GNP to the effort, but Hungarian environmentalists wonder whether this will be enough.

Over half of Hungary's air pollution originates in neighbouring countries – primarily West and East Germany and Czechoslovakia. Conversely, more than 10% of Romania's SO_2 is Hungarian in origin. Hungary also sends out much of its annual SO_2 production of 1.4 million tonnes to Austria, Czechoslovakia and Yugoslavia. Hungary – a member of the 30% Club – reduced its SO_2 emissions by 13% between 1980 and 1985, and is planning a 30% reduction by 1990. But it is also planning increased reliance on poor quality lignite, so the reality may be closer to a 55% increase in emissions.[42]

Unless these countries make a concerted effort to co-ordinate emission control measures or to provide funds for fuel cleaning or post-combustion control measures, the projected increase in SO_2 emissions could cause serious environmental problems.[43] It also appears that large areas of Hungarian soil are acidified, with consequent leaching of nutrients and the risk of contaminated groundwater.

Hungary has long been heavily dependent on imported oil as an energy source, but one the objectives of Hungary's new energy strategy is to move away from oil as soon as possible. New processing techniques should make it possible to increase the use of existing coal resources threefold by the year 2000.[44] Hungary has one nuclear power plant, at Paks. Hungary's more modern power plants are equipped with electrostatic precipitators, which eliminate dust and fly ash, but not SO_2. However, the most serious sources of air pollution in the country are not power plants but motor vehicles and home heating units in cities. Air pollution from home heating systems is being controlled by connecting more than 200,000 homes to district heating networks, and encouraging the use of natural gas in Budapest. Since both motor vehicles and home heating units produce large quantities of NO_x, the only way to reduce air pollution significantly in the long run in urban areas is to build large-scale district-heating systems and introduce pollution controls on all vehicles – a strategy that is likely to take decades to implement.[45]

The East European environmental dilemma has encouraged co-operation between states in the area on the exchange of information, and talks between East and West Germany and between Austria and Hungary on shared problems. There are active citizens' groups in several countries, growing popular pressures for changes in policy, and more open criticism and discussion in the wake of glasnost. It remains to be seen what changes the current trends towards more open elections in countries like the Soviet Union and Poland will bring. The crux of the problem is the potential political disquiet about introducing environmental reforms that may interfere with national production goals, or even lead to a rethinking of nuclear power plans. But the alternatives – declining forest resources, impaired health, polluted rivers and acidified soils – are likely to be even more expensive in the long term.

NOTES

1. Glenny, Misha, "Living in a socialist smog", in *New Scientist*, 24 September 1987.
2. Engels, Friedrich, "Part played by labour in the transition from ape to man", in *Dialectics of Nature* (Moscow: Progress, 1976).
3. Ziegler, Charles, *Environmental Policy in the Soviet* (Amherst: University of Massachusetts Press, 1987).
4. *Newsweek* , 14 January 1985.
5. Soviet Report to the Multilateral Conference on the Environment, Munich, 24–27 June 1984 (unpublished).
6. See note 5.
7. Quoted in Elsworth, Steve, *Acid Rain* (London: Pluto Press, 1984).
8. Soviet Report to Munich, see note 5.
9. Komarov, Boris, *The Destruction of Nature in the Soviet Union* (London: Pluto Press, 1978)
10. United Nations, *National Strategies and Policies for Air Pollution Abatement* (New York: United Nations, 1987).
11. Soviet Report to Munich, see note 5.
12. Ziegler, see note 3.
13. Perera, Judith, "Where glasnost meets the greens", in *New Scientist* 8 October 1988, pp 25–6.
14. Perera, see note 13.
15. Ziegler, see note 3.
16. East German Report to the Multilateral Conference on the Environment, Munich, 24–27 June 1984 (unpublished).
17. *Skogen* (Forest), Sweden, March 1984.
18. East German Report to Munich, see note 16.
19. See note 16.
20. Quoted in *Der Spiegel* , No. 12, 1984.
21. Czechoslovak Academy of Sciences, *An Analysis of the Ecological Situation in Czechoslovakia* (unpublished), 1983.
22. Glenny, see note 1.
23. See note 1.
24. See note 1.
25. See note 1.
26. Quoted in Don Hinrichsen "Acid rain and forest decline", in Edward Goldmith and Nicholas Hildyard, (eds), *The Earth Report: The Essential*

Guide to Global Ecological Issues (Los Angeles: Price, Stern Sloan Inc., 1988).

27. *New Scientist*, 27 September 1984.

28. Czechoslovakian Report to the Multilateral Conference on the Environment, Munich, 24–27 June 1984 (unpublished).

29. Glenny, see note 1.

30. Serafin, Rafal, "The greening of Poland", in *The Ecologist* 12:4, July/August 1982, pp. 176–184.

31. See note 30.

32. See note 30.

33. See note 30.

34. Pudlis, Eugeniusz, "Poland's plight: environment damaged from air pollution and acid rain", in *Ambio* 12:1, 1983, pp. 125–27.

35. Polish Report to the Multilateral Conference on the Environment, Munich, 24–27 June 1984 (unpublished).

36. Serafin, see note 30.

37. Pudlis, see note 34.

38. Timberlake, Lloyd, "Poland – the most polluted country in the world?", in *New Scientist*, 22 October 1981.

39. Pudlis, see note 34.

39. See note 34.

40. Romanian Report to the Multilateral Conference on the Environment, Munich, 24–27 June 1984 (unpublished).

41. Quoted in Elsworth, see note 7.

42. Jszay, T. and G. Bede, "Energy and environment in Hungary", in *Ambio* 13:2, 1984, pp. 107–108.

43. See note 42.

44. See note 42.

45. See note 42.

9. The Third World – Pollution and Development

Industry and acid pollution usually go together, which is why most people think of acid rain as a North American or European problem. It is rarely associated with less developed countries (LDCs). Yet there is growing evidence of acid pollution in south-east Asia, Latin America and even in southern Africa. There is little immediate prospect of it being stopped, and every prospect of it becoming worse.

A joint project between the UN Environment Programme (UNEP) and SCOPE (a committee of the International Council of Scientific Unions) was launched in 1984 to study acidification in tropical countries. It planned to assess the potential for acid pollution if SO_2 and NO_x emissions were to increase, to identify the most susceptible areas, and to investigate the need for monitoring. Among the countries to be studied were Brazil, Mexico, India, Kenya, Malaysia, Nigeria, China and Venezuela. Under the auspices of SCOPE, the Conference on Acidification of Tropical Ecosystems was held in Caracas, Venezuela in April 1986. Case studies from Australia, Bangladesh, Brazil, China, India, Nigeria and Venezuela were prepared for the conference. There was little immediate evidence of serious regional acidification (with the notable exception of China),[1] but it was generally agreed that sulphur emissions were likely to increase as industrialization proceeded, and several of the cases studies found high levels of acidity and low alkilinity.

LDCs as yet account for only a small proportion of global commercial energy consumption, but the proportion is growing (see Table 9.1). In 1973, the Third World accounted for 16% of total world commercial energy consumption; by 1986, the proportion had risen to 24%.[2] Between 1970 and 1986, world commercial energy consumption grew by 45%, and European consumption by 27%; in Asia, by contrast, consumption grew by 120%.[3] Furthermore, consumption is heavily concentrated: the 12 largest LDCs account for more than

Table 9.1: Commercial energy consumption, 1986

	Total consumption (peta-joules)	Growth since 1970 (%)
West and East Europe	64 177	27
USSR	52 671	80
US and Canada	74 066	18
Mexico	3 806	144
Brazil	3 088	153
Rest of Latin America	6 536	–
China	21 771	158
India	6 160	175
Japan	12 900	32
Rest of Asia	17 283	–
Oceania	3 635	75
South Africa	3 111	87
Rest of Africa	3 998	–
LDC total	65 753	–
WORLD	**273 202**	**45**

Source: WRI/IIED, *World Resources 1988–89* (New York: Basic Books, 1988).

two-thirds of all LDC commercial energy consumption. China alone accounts for about a third of the LDC total (and for two-thirds of coal consumption); Brazil, India and Mexico together account for another 20%.

The choking cities of the Third World

The worst pollution usually comes with the biggest cities. Air pollution has not yet been banished from the cities of Europe and North America, but at least tighter controls are being imposed. In the Third

World, where the growth of cities is often rapid and unregulated, air pollution is worsening and there is little immediate prospect of it being curbed. While the rural population of LDCs barely doubled between 1920 and 1980, the urban population grew ninefold.[4] In 1950, 17% of the Third World's population lived in cities; by the year 2000, the figure is expected to be nearly 44% (in Latin America the proportion is already closer to 70–75%, the same as Europe). In 1980, 8 of the world's 15 largest (and most polluted) urban centres were in the Third World including Mexico City, Sao Paulo, Shanghai, Beijing and Rio de Janeiro.[5]

Although the Third World (excluding China) had only 11% of the world's industrial production in 1980,[6] its industry tends to be highly concentrated – by region and by country – and growth has been rapid. More than 35 LDCs recorded annual average industrial production growth rates of 5% or more during the 1960s and 1970s.[7] To add to the problem, the tightening of pollution laws in more developed countries (MDCs) has meant that multinational corporations have been tempted to transfer so-called "dirty industries" (including metal smelters) to LDCs with less stringent regulations. For example, Japanese and North American companies have transferred production to countries like Taiwan, South Korea, the Philippines and Thailand. Between 1985 and 1990, the capacity of coal-fired power plants in south-east Asia is expected to have expanded from 2,000 MW to about 25,000 MW. This will raise coal consumption from 3 million tonnes to 60 million tonnes in a decade. Uncontrolled combustion of coal with an average sulphur content of 1% could lead to annual SO_2 emissions of more than a million tonnes in a region where the soils are moderately to highly susceptible to acidification.

Despite new environmental laws, new state and local environment agencies, and the lobbying of many increasingly active non-governmental groups, pollution in many Third World cities is going from bad to worse. NO_x, ozone and particulate levels are often critical; as the size of cities increases, so will the use and concentration of road traffic. Many vehicles are poorly maintained, and the introduction of unleaded petrol in LDCs is unlikely in the foreseeable future, so the concentration of airborne pollutants will increase accordingly. Concentrated urban pollution in the Third World is beginning to have the same kinds of effects on surrounding countryside as it is in

Northern cities. A study of pollution in China by Professor Vaclav Smil of the University of Manitoba suggests that reported cases of damage to crops downwind of Chinese industrial centres are "most certainly just the proverbial tip of the iceberg".[8] This comment could apply equally to other Third World nations experiencing rapid industrial growth. For instance, there are reports of damage to the once important rice-growing Samsson plains in South Korea, caused by power and petrochemical plants, and copper and zinc smelters.[9]

South-east Asian cities are facing particular problems. Many share a peculiar characteristic which increases the likelihood of concentrations of smog and ozone production – and hence of acid deposition. The commercial centres of these cities are often several degrees warmer than the surrounding countryside, a phenomenon that creates "heat islands" which, in calm conditions, produce a circular airflow above a city. Dr Sham Sani, a geographer at Malaysia's Kebangsaan University, warns that air pollution problems in Metro Manila and other cities of south-east Asia are likely to be worse than those in some North American cities. The Philippines National Pollution Control Commission warned in 1979 that industry and road vehicles in Manila (which harbours 63% of the country's industrial firms) discharged substantial quantities of air pollutants.[10] Hong Kong faces similar problems. One of the most densely populated areas in the world, it is home to 5 million people and different activities are not segregated. Industrial areas rub shoulders with residential areas. Industry, overpopulation and thousands of motor vehicles cause serious air pollution; levels of SO_2, NO_x, CO and lead are high.

Air pollution is a major health hazard in many of Malaysia's main urban centres. According to the Director General of the government's Environment Division, the highly urbanized Kelan valley, which includes Kuala Lumpur, has a pollution level two to three times higher than that of major US cities.[11] As early as 1977 the Ministry of Science, Technology and Environment estimated that Malaysia was annually emitting 635,000 tonnes of pollutants, and that the total was increasing annually by 10%. The source of 45% of the pollutants is road traffic. The number of vehicles on Malaysian roads has been rising rapidly: from 670,000 in 1970 to 2.6 million in 1982 in peninsular Malaysia. Badly maintained engines and the high lead content of fuel make the emissions worse. Annual NO_x emissions are likely to be at least 200,000 tonnes and lead emissions, 2,000 tonnes.[12] In Kuala Lumpur, road vehicles are thought to account for about 92% of pollutants in the air.[13] In 1975, emission controls were introduced under the Road Traffic Ordinance, but they applied only to diesel-powered vehicles.

Clean air regulations introduced in Kuala Lumpur in 1978 appear to have had little effect. Readings from air-quality samplers have revealed suspended particulate densities of between 118 and 313 microgrammes per cubic metre, well above the World Health Organization (WHO) guideline of 40–60 microgrammes.[14] Ozone levels rise from near zero in the early morning to 0.06 parts per million between midday and early afternoon. (The WHO recommended limit is 0.06 ppm for a maximum of one hour). Industrial emissions are a more localized problem. A major industrial polluter is the Datuk Keramat smelting plant in George Town, on Penang Island. The Malaysian Meteorological Department has run a limited monitoring programme since 1976, using standard World Meteorological Organization procedures. Monthly samples of rainfall in Petaling Jaya (outside Kuala Lumpur) and Tanah Rata (in Perak) returned pH readings of 4.4–4.8 and 4.9–5.5 respectively.[15]

Under the Environmental Quality Act of 1974, a Division of Environment (DoE) was set up under the Ministry of Science, Technology and Environment to regulate environmental quality. It has the power to issue regulations and orders on pollution control and to issue licences to regulate the discharge of wastes. A number of regulations have since been issued, but the DoE is required only to see that pollution levels do not exceed "acceptable" levels, a definition which Sahabat Alam Malaysia (SAM – Friends of the Earth Malaysia) believes makes a mockery of the concept of environmental management. SAM argues that the DoE "simply ignores the issue of pollution", and that environmental quality will continue to remain an issue of low priority "as long as politicians and government officials still think that emphasis on environmental management will affect foreign and local investment and economic growth".[16]

The Asian miracle: productivity and pollution

Australians and west-coast Americans readily boast that the Pacific rim is the economic growth centre of the future, if not the present. From Seattle to Seoul, from Santiago to Sydney, industry and new technology are producing a welter of new products that are changing the expectations of global consumers. The United States is looking increasingly to Japan as its principal economic partner (or competitor). Nowhere has the growth been more spectacular than in the newly industrialized countries (NICs): South Korea, Taiwan, Hong Kong and Singapore. But just as night follows day, pollution is following industrial growth. Low prices are often made possible by lax planning laws, and the NICs are beginning to find that one of the prices of rapid and relatively unrestrained industrial growth is growing air and water pollution. But where the NICs – like Japan before them – may have the resources and the planners to eventually curb pollution, the less developed countries of south and south-east Asia are not so well placed. China, India, Indonesia, Malaysia and the Philippines are all experiencing worsening air pollution. The Pacific rim may be the industrial giant of the future but it may also be the site of growing acid pollution.

Early research in China suggests that the scale of air pollution there may be worse even than among China's socialist cousins in eastern Europe. Coal-burning has increased at a pace to match China's industrial development, but so has pollution. The concentration of energy consumption in a few sprawling urban areas – including Beijing, Shanghai, Lanzhou and Shenyang – has made the prospect of severe localized acid pollution even greater. Further west, the inefficacy of India's pollution controls and zoning laws was tragically emphasized in 1984 with the death of more than 3,000 people at Bhopal. In the race to develop a strong industrial base, India – like many less developed countries – has tended to forget external costs such as pollution. The result is smog-choked cities, growing threats to human health, and the prospect of serious acid pollution.

China

China ranks third after the United States and the USSR in consumption of primary commercial energy and production of SO_2.

But unlike either of those countries, where efforts are being made to reduce pollutive emissions, pollution in China is worsening. China is still one of the poorest countries on earth, with a per capita gross national product (GNP) of about $300–500, but it has set out on a programme of rapid economic development. Gross industrial output has been growing at an average 12% annually, and the percentage share of industry in gross domestic product (GDP) grew from less than 10% in 1952 to 43% in 1984.[17] This is all well and good, but much of Chinese industry suffers from muddled management and lax planning laws, and much of it is concentrated in Shandong and Jiangsu provinces in the east, and Guangdong province in the south. One of the results is that China may yet prove to be one of the most polluted countries on earth, with the potential for serious and widespread acid pollution. Monitoring is patchy, research is still in its formative stages, and confirmed incidents of acid deposition are rare, but air pollution from coal-burning is already sufficiently serious in major urban centres – particularly in the south – to merit real concern.

Pollution was long a non-issue in China, at least in part because of the priority given to economic development. Thanks to its isolation and the anti-intellectual foment of the Cultural Revolution, the environmental movement of the 1960s largely bypassed China. This began to change with the decline of Mao, the rise of new pragmatic leaders, the growing openness of China, and the new awareness of global environmental problems that followed the 1972 UN Conference on the Human Environment in Stockholm.[18] During the mid 1970s, China paid new attention to the more practical problems of development, beginning with a national conference on environmental protection held in Beijing in 1973. Only the year before, the Chinese position at Stockholm had been highly confrontational, based on a suspicion that the environmental movement in capitalist countries was an attempt to reduce or prevent development in the Third World.[19] Now, the State Planning Commission agreed in principle to the notion that environmental planning need not compromise economic development.

An Environmental Protection Office (EPO) was created in 1974 and, by 1979, draft environmental protection statutes had been drawn up for the seven most industrialized provinces in the north and east.[20]

The EPO has since been superceded by a new state bureau with greater powers, and funding for environmental protection has been growing steadily. Ross notes the importance to these policy changes of a new, more tolerant leadership, and of greater openness and communication among Chinese environmentalists and scientists. However, popular protest has been another factor. In 1979 alone, Shanghai reported 339 instances of confrontation between factories and the public over pollution, resulting in 49 full or partial shutdowns.[21] The Chinese people are clearly becoming more concerned about pollution, and the leadership (until the events of May-June 1989 at least) had shown itself more willing to hear their protests.

While the policy prospects for environmental protection in China seem to be improving, the country remains heavily polluted, thanks to its heavy reliance on coal, which provides about 70–75% of Chinese primary energy needs. Annual coal production increased more than 20 times between 1949 and 1982; annual present production stands at about 660 million tonnes, and consumption at about 600 million tonnes. The threat of acid pollution arises not so much from the quantity of coal consumed as from its quality. First, although the sulphur content of Chinese coal is low (2–3% on average, but as low as 0.5%),[22] China (unlike most major coal-producing countries where coal is washed before use) cleans only 17%. Second, combustion is generally inefficient. China converts just 30% of its fuel into useful energy (compared to 40–55% in North America and Europe, and 60% in Japan). Third, energy consumption is concentrated in a few major cities.

The cumulative result is that China produces about 18 million tonnes of SO_2 annually,[23] 85% of which comes from coal burning. Only the Soviet Union and the United States produce more. Much of this comes from industry and coal-burning power stations, but about 35–40% of total SO_2 emissions come from the small domestic stoves which account for 60% of China's coal consumption.[24] As Chinese industry continues to grow, more coal will be burned, increasing the prospects for acid pollution. The southern provinces of China, particularly those south of the Yangtze, are likely to be at highest risk from soil and water acidification. Soils and surface waters in the area are generally acidic and the soils are poorly buffered. The particle content of the air is much lower and the pH of rainwater is 4.5–5.5.[25]

Although the levels of sulphur emitted by domestic coal burning are lower than in the north, this is being offset by a rapid industrialization programme which demands increased amounts of energy. Cities which use high-sulphur coal and where stagnant air currents are common – such as Chongqing and Guiyang in the south-west – are recording concentrations of atmospheric SO_2 as high as 347 micrograms per cubic metre.[26] Beijing meanwhile records SO_2 concentrations as high as 167 in city centre commercial areas, and 228 in city centre residential areas. Peak levels as high as 625 have been recorded in Beijing and as high as 1,119 in Shenyang. These are among the highest levels in the world. By comparison, Athens, London and New York recorded levels of 46, 49 and 65 between 1982 and 1985 with peak figures in the range of 116–171 (see Table 9.2). (The WHO guideline is in the range of 40–60 micrograms/cu.m.).

Acid rain monitoring began in Shanghai and Songjiang counties in March 1980, and measured Shanghai's first recorded acid rain storm in September 1981.[27] Nationwide acid rain monitoring began in 1982; records to date have shown frequent rainstorms south of the Yangtze with a pH of less than 5.6. The most acid rain (with a pH of 4.14 and 4.02 respectively) has been recorded in Chongqing and Guiyang.[28]

In the northern part of the country, cities like Beijing and Lanzhou give cause for the greatest concern. In the Xigu district of Lanzhou (a new industrial city in the north-west, containing some of the country's largest chemical industries and oil refineries), pollution has destroyed fruit trees, caused date plants to stop producing fruit, and stopped pumpkins from maturing. Beijing, which relies on coal for three-quarters of its energy needs, consumes eight million tonnes per year. The major consumers are power plants, 10,000 small boilers in offices and factories, and about a million household stoves. The stoves and boilers are highly inefficient, emitting about 20 kg (44 lb) of SO_2 per tonne of coal burned (200,000 tonnes per year).

Yet the dangers in the north are offset to a large extent by relatively high levels of soil alkalinity. Although there is a risk of acid precipitation, the soil releases ammonia into the air, helping to neutralize the effect of acid pollution. Measurements of the rain have shown pH values of 7.0–7.5. Beijing is known for its high concentration of

Table 9.2: Sulphur dioxide concentrations in major urban areas, 1976–85 (in micrograms per cubic metre).

THIRD WORLD CITIES IN BOLD TYPE

City	Mean of daily values			Peak levels		
	1976–78	1979–81	1982–85	1976–78	1979–81	1982–85
Beijing	–	66	167	–	290	459
Shenyang	–	72	160	–	320	576
Seoul[1]	–	–	137	–	–	474
Tehran	65	129	122	183	362	467
Milan	226	171	108	686	530	406
Rio de Janeiro	64	115	86	161	227	279
Santiago	76	63	85	221	205	188
Manila	67	73	83	170	137	161
Guangzhou	–	117	81	–	340	206
Sao Paulo[2]	121	131	80	294	327	173
Brussels	98	77	71	305	273	205
Calcutta	43	65	68	217	288	188
New York City[2]	72	74	65	167	203	116
Madrid	97	108	64	301	333	193
Stockholm	–	58	62	149	174	–
Hong Kong	12	37	62	87	117	121

Cities at or below the WHO guideline of 40–60 micrograms per cubic metre

Frankfurt	84	73	59	231	224	230
Shanghai	–	65	54	–	272	217
London	108	67	49	322	216	171
Warsaw	43	44	39	215	198	188
Caracas	21	30	31	37	44	49
Helsinki	25	22	28	104	82	67
Montreal	54	44	25	192	166	85
Tokyo	63	47	25	111	91	58
Vancouver	–	9	15	–	26	59
Bogota	15	3	14	37	15	70
Toronto	–	21	12	–	79	66
Bombay	26	23	8	123	97	38

Note: all monitoring sites are city centre commercial except [1]suburban industrial, and [2]city centre residential.

Source: WHO and UNEP figures in WRI/IIED, *World Resources 1988–89* (New York: Basic Books, 1988).

suspended particulates, about half of which is desert dust and half is fly ash from coal combustion.[29] Measurements in the city during 1979–80 found that, even though there were high concentrations of sulphate and nitrate ions, rainwater was not abnormally acidic. Investigators concluded that the concentration of suspended matter in the water neutralized the acids. In 1983, however, it was reported that Beijing rainwater was slightly acid (pH 5.0–5.5).[30]

The most worrying problems relate to human health. Emissions of SO_2 and other pollutants are thought to be linked, for example, with the higher than average incidence of lung cancer in Chinese cities: 17–31 cases per 100,000 people, compared to 4–5 per 100,000 in rural areas.[31] The incidence of lung cancer in Shanghai grew from 5.25 cases per 100,000 in 1960 to 35 per 100,000 in 1976,[32] due at least in part to worsening air pollution (but also due to the high numbers of smokers in China). One estimate is that air pollution causes an annual loss of more than 3.5 million working days, and 6,000 premature deaths (mainly among newborn babies and elderly people with chronic heart or lung disease).[33] The effect of coal combustion in the cities is made worse by the fact that most emissions come from low chimneys, so the pollutants concentrate close to the ground, especially during autumn and winter thermal inversions. In the absence of emission controls, observes Vaclav Smil, this provides a perfect setting for the repetition of acute air pollution episodes such as those that occurred in London in 1952.[34] Hazy winter days have become a characteristic of northern Chinese cities.

Plans to expand coal-fired electricity generation may increase the risks of acid pollution. A proposed concentration of power stations in Shaanxi, China's richest coal province, could create major SO_2 and NO_x emissions that would be carried south/south-east in winter and north/north-west in summer, affecting the farmlands of the North China plain and the Nei Monggol pastures. Planned power stations at Jilin would produce summer emissions that would be carried over Da Hinggan, China's richest boreal forest.[35]

Despite the creation of new environmental management agencies, and the apparently pragmatic attitude of China's leaders (until recently), controlling pollution and curbing acid deposition in China promises to be difficult. There are no cheap, readily available alternative sources of commercial energy, and the costs of replacing outdated combustion equipment or installing emission controls may be prohibitively expensive. Energy is being used more efficiently in some areas (industrial output in the 32 largest cities rose by 10% in 1980, while primary energy use fell by 4.6%), but this will need to be applied far more widely to have any appreciable effect. There is also the real possibility that emissions from cities like Beijing and Shanghai are being blown across the Yellow Sea and the East China Sea to Korea and Japan. Research is still in its formative stages, but the next few years could reveal an international acid rain problem in south-east Asia that parallels the situations in North America and Europe.

India

India is a major coal producer and consumer. Production in 1982 was 125 million tonnes and is expected to increase to around 325 million tonnes in 1995.[36] Annual SO_2 emissions tripled from the early 1960s to reach 3.2 million tonnes in 1979.[37] This is a modest figure by Chinese standards, and amounts to a miniscule per capita rate. Indian coal also has a generally low sulphur content (less than 1%), but the projected increases in coal consumption could push SO_2 emissions closer to seven million tonnes by 1995. To make matters worse, much of that is going to be concentrated in a few major urban centres, posing the threat of worsening acid pollution. NO_x emissions are also likely to rise with the growth in road traffic and the operations of fertilizer plants, refineries, and petrochemical and other industries.

Coal-fired thermal power stations provide nearly 65% of India's electricity. Although they use low-sulphur coal, the coal has a high ash content (25–40%). Older plants are fitted with mechanical dust collectors that generally operate at about 70% efficiency, and newer plants have electrostatic precipitators which can remove up to 99% of dust if properly maintained. But breakdowns regularly lead to pollution. For example, a breakdown of precipitators in the Bhatinda power station in the Punjab in the early 1980s resulted in 1,200 tonnes of fly ash being emitted into the atmosphere every year. In 1982, *India Today* reported that the town of Bhatinda (which received no power itself from the plant) lay under "a permanent blanket of smoke; fly ash coats every surface and a good deep breath is likely to wind up a racking cough".[38] The Delhi-based Centre for Science and Environment (CSE) warned in 1983 that air pollution, "after engulfing the large cities of India, ... has begun to hurt the residents of small towns and once sleepy villages where thermal power stations and large industries are now being located".[39] The CSE observed that while urban communities have pressure groups and officials to whom protests can be made, effective protest in villages can take longer to emerge.

India's Sixth Five Year Plan (1980–85), while noting the country's advantages (low-sulphur coal, relatively few automobiles, and a rainy season that is an effective air scrubber), pointed out that air pollution was becoming severe in cities like Calcutta, Bombay and Delhi, and levels of SO_2 and particulate matter in some bigger cities exceeded WHO guidelines. Every major Indian city is now thought to suffer from chemical air pollution.[40] SO_2 concentrations in Calcutta have been growing steadily: from a daily mean of 43 micrograms per cubic metre in downtown commercial areas in 1976–78 to 68 in 1982–85, with peak levels as high as 188.[41] Half of Delhi's air pollution is thought to come from domestic fuel burning.[42] The CSE pointed out that India's uncontrolled industries and badly maintained automobiles may be fewer in number, but they rival those in the West in their pollutive capacity. Reducing air pollution levels in Indian cities, it suggests, could involve popularizing the use of efficient stoves, setting and enforcing emission control standards for motor vehicles, limiting traffic in congested or ill-ventilated streets, and carrying out air quality surveys.

The attitude of planners and developers is exemplified by the comment of a senior executive of Graphite India, who argued that pollution "is the price society must pay if it wants modern society to thrive – if we close down, society will have to pay a higher price [than mere pollution]".[43] India, like many LDCs, faces a struggle between demands for economic growth and an improved standard of living, and demands for a healthy living environment with a minimum of pollutive side-effects. The Department of the Environment was created in 1980 under the office of the prime minister, and was charged – among other things – with monitoring pollution. By 1985, 18 out of India's 22 states had their own environment departments, and there were more than 200 national and state laws relating to the environment.[44] This sounds impressive on paper, but in practice it has achieved little. A recent survey found that many of the new laws promote development and resource use *without* careful analysis of the possible environmental effects; several state laws have potentially adverse effects on neighbouring states; many of the laws are simply inadequate; and the environment is such a new policy area that within government it is commonly ignored or overlooked.[45]

Southern and eastern parts of India contain soils susceptible to acidification. Professor D.N. Rao of the Banaras Hindu University warns that agricultural yields could drop by 17–30% depending on the level of future emissions. Professor Rao has reported damage to plant life in the Mirzapur district in Uttar Pradesh.[46] A case study from a sulphuric acid plant showed that the estimated loss of mango crops alone amounted to thousands of rupees. When emission control equipment – including acid mist eliminators – was installed, it added 0.2% to the production costs and cut concentrations of gaseous pollutants by 90%.[47] A study by the Institute of Science in Bombay found that mango trees along road sides were visibly damaged by air pollutants; up to 30% of the tree leaves died, and trees in areas surrounding the Hindustan Petroleum Refinery were destroyed.[48]

The problems facing the Taj Mahal illustrate the threat to India's cultural heritage. In 1982, a major oil refinery was opened outside Mathura City, just 40 km (25 miles) upwind from the Taj Mahal in Agra, and upwind from other monuments in Fatehpur-Sikri, Matura and Brindavan. The refinery processes 6.2 million tonnes of crude oil annually. There were fears from the outset that the pollution caused by the refinery would slowly destroy the Taj Mahal, although government officials denied the possibility. An Italian consultancy firm brought in to advise on the environmental consequences of the refinery concluded that SO_2 emissions would be insufficient to damage the Taj, and that the existing discolouration of marble and sandstone in monuments in the vicinity was due to algae and fungi rather than pollutants. Even so, on the basis that the threat to the Taj could be minimized by controlling emissions from other sources in the area, two thermal power stations were closed and coal-burning railway locomotives were replaced by diesel powered engines.

Professor J.M. Dave of the School of Environmental Sciences at Jawarhalal Nehru University in New Delhi predicted that the refinery would annually emit 25–30 tonnes of SO_2, 100–150 tonnes of carbon monoxide, 60–100 tonnes of hydrocarbons, 100 tonnes of NO_x and trace metals like vanadium, nickel, cadmium and chromium, most of which would be blown by the north-westerly winds in October and March from Mathura to Agra. Professor Dave warned that increased acidity would "definitely damage the marble of the Taj irreparably over a period of 50 to 100 years. The delicate carved projection may crumble even earlier, being converted into gypsum."

Latin America: pockets of heavy pollution

Data on actual or potential acid pollution in Latin America are variable, but there are enough known instances of isolated pockets of heavy pollution (notably in and around major cities) to suggest that acid pollution is a real danger. A recent informal survey by Associated Press concluded that acid pollution was a "serious problem" in Brazil, Mexico and Chile, and that it had been reported in Argentina and Peru. Local environmentalists warn of the dangers: "It's very serious", says Paulo Nogueira Neto, head of Brazil's environment agency. "In some areas the damage is obvious, but it could be occurring in other places that we don't know about."

There are three short-term barriers to action. First, acid pollution is not a public issue and is not generally perceived as being a problem. It is such a new phenomenon (in the Latin American context) that many people, including government officials, have never even heard of it. Second, the lack of reliable data undermines the case for action. Third, the priorities of development and the economic burden of often massive foreign debts make pollution control – in the eyes of many governments – a minor concern. A 1982 report by the Sao Paulo Federation of Industries in Brazil observed that Brazil must "choose between pollution and recession".[49] But the experience of three countries in particular – Brazil, Venezuela, and Mexico – suggests that policymakers might be well advised to start acquainting themselves with the problem.

Brazil

Brazil has become infamous in the last two decades for the rapid and massive clearance of its tropical rain forests. But it also faces severe localized air pollution, particularly in the south-western states of Sao Paulo, Rio de Janeiro, Minas Gerais, Parana and Rio Grande do Sul. Cubatao, near Sao Paulo, is one of the most polluted industrial areas in the world, perhaps rivalled only by the industrial centres of Poland and Czechoslovakia. Situated in a valley, and home to 15,000 people (most of them low-income workers), Cubatao's air contains 1,200 micrograms of industrial particles per cubic metre, *twice* the amount considered lethal by WHO. Thirty-three factories daily emit 1,000 tonnes of SO_2, NO_x, CO, hydrocarbons and dust. Development in the area began in the early 1950s with four large multinational companies; today there are 19. Fish die in the reddish local water, trees are reduced to dry skeletons, and 80% of the flora is gone. Human health also suffers. In 1981 it was revealed that 17 out of the 3,400 newborn children in Cubatao died from anacephalia (a rare disorder that causes children to be born without a brain or other parts of the body). The normal rate of anacephalia in newborn babies in Latin America is one in every 5,000. In Cubatao it was one in 200. In August 1984 the Sao Paulo state environmental office announced an emergency four-year programme for reducing air pollution in Cubatao by 90%, at an estimated cost to the industries involved of $150 million.[50] The results are still awaited.

Commercial energy consumption in Brazil grew by more than 150% between 1970 and 1986. Most of its coal reserves consist of lignite or sub-bituminous coal, so air pollution is likely to grow steadily worse. Brazil has some coal reserves, and consumption is rising by about 10% per year. Air pollution is now considered "normal" in most Brazilian cities. Research on acidification is still in its formative stages, but soil samples from the eastern parts of Sao Paulo state have already shown extremely low pH values (3.7–4.7). Large areas of Brazil consist of naturally acid soils; 75% of the Amazon Basin has acid, infertile, well-weathered soils deficient in plant nutrients. The aluminium content of these soils is so high that it can be toxic to plants, hence acid deposition would have serious ecological implications.

Venezuela

Venezuela is the seventh largest oil producer in the world; oil and oil products together account for 96% of export earnings. Most of the oil – which is generally high in sulphur – comes from the area around Lake Maracaibo in the north-west. Large reserves have also been discovered by the Orinoco. Industries – including refineries and petrochemical plants – are concentrated in the north and north-west. In the east where the Orinoco and Caroni rivers meet, a major new city, Ciudad Guayana, is being constructed. It includes a centre of heavy industry.

In 1983, the director of environmental protection in the Venezuelan environment ministry, Roberto Yoshiba, warned that there was potential for acid rain in Venezuela.[51] NO emissions from road traffic present the biggest problem at the moment; Caracas alone has more than 500,000 cars. SO_2 concentrations are still below WHO guidelines, but they are growing steadily. Yoshiba warned that there were several "risk areas" where industries were using sulphur-rich fossil fuels. These included thermal power stations at Planta Centro and Tacoa in the far west of Venezuela and a petrochemical complex at Moron (west of Caracas).

Another future source of emissions is the heavy-crude treatment plant planned for the Orinoco oilfields, which started processing oil in 1988. This poses a potential threat to the nearby Uverido forest reserve and the town of Ciudad Bolivar, 30 km (19 miles) away. The state petroleum company, Petroleos de Venezuela, claims that SO_2 emissions from the plant would not be sufficient to affect Uverido. Yoshiba is less certain, but financial cutbacks in the environment ministry have meant that he has not had the funds to carry out adequate monitoring programmes.

Given the sensitivity of soils in the north and the area's concentrations of cities and industry, there are also risks of environmental damage from acidifying emissions. The large-scale extraction of tar sands at Orinoco could contribute to the future acidification of Venezuelan soils and waters. Venezuelan tar sands (like those in Canada, Colombia and the United States) reportedly contain as much petroleum as the oil fields in the Middle East, but the economic and environmental costs of extracting oil from tar sands are high.

Mexico

Mexico City is one of the most polluted cities in the world, so much so that in October 1984 Mayor Ramon Aguirre Velazquez warned of "collective hysteria" unless dramatic controlling measures were taken.[52] Smog in January 1989 was so bad that schoolchildren were given the month off. On 312 days in 1988, smog levels exceeded WHO guidelines.[53] The city's position in a valley surrounded by mountains creates a temperature inversion in the hot months of February to May that combines with heavy city traffic to produce a brown, noxious photochemical smog. This contains ozone and other oxidants, and often reduces visibility to three or four city blocks.

Three-quarters of Mexico's cars and most of its commercial vehicles are found in the Mexico City area. The city population has grown from 1.7 million to 18 million since 1940, and by the end of the century is expected to be close to 26 million, making it the biggest city in the world. Mexican fuel consumption is rising accordingly: by 59% between 1979 and 1982 alone. Trees are already dying along the most heavily travelled corridors in the city. Emissions from the city's 130,000 factories add to the daily output of 11,000 tonnes of particulates into the air. For seven months of the year, winds are too weak to disperse these and other emissions. Polluted air sits stolidly over the city, posing a serious threat to human health.

Mexico has estimated oil reserves of 40 billion barrels, and crude oil accounts for 71% of export earnings. Newly discovered oil reserves in Mexico, Venezuela and the Caribbean are believed to be in the same order of magnitude as known reserves in the Middle East. The Mexican oil fields are mainly concentrated on the eastern coast, in the Mexican Gulf, on the US border and south of Veracruz. Prevailing winds in Mexico indicate that pollutants from refineries and industrial centres on the east coast may well be deposited in agricultural areas (coffee, sugar cane) on the coast and to the east of Mexico City. The Yucatan Peninsula, in particular, has soils that are likely to be susceptible to acidification.

Southern Africa: pollution on the highveld

With few concentrations of heavy industry, relatively few densely populated urban conurbations, and deriving most of its energy needs from non-commercial fuels such as firewood, acid pollution is a distant concern in most of Africa. There are, however, two notable exceptions: South Africa and Zambia.

To all intents and purposes, South Africa is an industrialized nation. It is also a major producer and consumer of coal, producing about a quarter of Africa's commercial energy and accounting for 43% of its coal consumption.[54] Bituminous coal provides all but a fraction of South African energy, half being consumed in electricity generation. Coal-burning causes estimated SO_2 emissions of about one million tonnes[55] (as much as the four Scandinavian countries combined). About 80% of the coal is burned within 200 km (125 miles) of the Witwatersrand (around Johannesburg) where the bulk of South African heavy industry is situated. This area includes the oil-from-coal plants run by state-owned Sasol, the largest company of its kind in the world. Sasol's Secunda plant alone emits 480 tonnes of SO_2 per day.[56] The area also supports power plants, iron works, chemical industry, paper and pulp industry, manufacturing industry and coal mining.

The area at greatest risk from acid deposition is the Eastern Transvaal highveld, which includes the Kruger National Park. The threat will grow if a planned expansion of coal-fired power stations is carried out in the region. In 1985 about 2,250 tonnes of SO_2 per day was emitted over the Eastern Transvaal. Thanks to stable local atmospheric conditions (particularly in the winter), 80% of the air pollutants stay within an area of some 3,000 sq km (1,150 sq miles), subjecting it to more than 220 tonnes of SO_2 per sq km. The Witwatersrand emissions also contain NO_x and other pollutants. No hard data are yet available on rainwater acidity or possible effects on rivers and groundwater, but rainwater measurement is planned and the Council for Scientific and Industrial Research is planning a five-year study. The first signs of corrosion to buildings in Johannesburg have been reported,[57] and archaeologists at the University of the Witwatersrand have stated that centuries-old engravings and Iron Age relics are suffering damage.

Further north, Zambia also faces the threat of acid pollution, thanks mainly to its copper industry. Commercial copper production began in Zambia in 1931. Although it has only really grown since the second world war, the air pollution created by SO_2 from smelting was already a health problem in the late 1930s. By 1979, copper accounted for nearly 91% of Zambia's exports. Mining and refining is concentrated in the most heavily urbanized area of the country – the eight towns that make up the Copperbelt – where nearly 60% of all urban dwellers live.

Copper ores contain a high proportion of sulphur, and the smelting process emits about 1,250 tonnes of SO_2 per day. Some is recovered to produce sulphuric acid, and there are plans to recover more and to change processing techniques to reduce emissions, but acid deposition has already been recorded. Much of this is dry deposition that falls in the vicinity of smelters, having an adverse effect on the growth of vegetable and fruit plants. Some meteorologists hold that the poor visibility frequently recorded at the airports at Kitwe and Ndola is a direct result of gaseous emissions, but this is disputed. Zambia Consolidated Copper Mines Ltd argues that meteorological conditions favour the rapid dispersal of stack emissions, and thermal inversion layers never last more than a few hours, so SO_2 emissions never build up to hazardous levels.[58]

A short monitoring programme carried out in Luanshya and Mufulira by Roan Consolidated Mining in 1980 found that levels of SO_2 in the atmosphere increased markedly during the dry winter months. Professor N.P. Perera of the University of Zambia believes that the mining companies have been "remarkably responsible" in their attitudes towards pollution. "In the absence of any legislation and at a time of financial difficulty they have made considerable efforts to evaluate the existing problems and introduce alternative production techniques." Nevertheless, he warns, SO_2 emissions remain a long-term problem over a wider area than the vicinity of the smelters, and could pose a hazard to the freshwater fishing industry, agriculture and forestry.[59] The Zambia National Conservation Strategy, published in January 1984, reached similar conclusions and noted that local damage to vegetation was already evident where sulphur compounds were generated by copper and zinc smelting.

NOTES

1. Whelan, T., "Acidification in the tropics: does it exist?", in *Ambio* 15:4 1986, pp. 252.
2. WRI/IIED, *World Resources 1988–89* (New York: Basic Books, 1988).
3. See note 2.
4. Hardoy, Jorge E. and David Satterthwaite, "Third World cities and the environment of poverty", in Robert Repetto, *The Global Possible* (New Haven: Yale University Press, 1985).
5. McAuslan, Patrick, *Urban Land and Shelter for the Poor* (London: Earthscan, 1985).
6. UNIDO, *A Statistical Review of the World Industrial Situation in 1980* (New York: UNIDO, 1981).
7. World Bank, *World Development Report* (Washington DC: World Bank, 1983).
8. Smil, Vaclav, *The Bad Earth: Environmental Degradation in China* (New York: Sharpe Zed, 1984).
9. Gennino, Angela and Tim Shorrock, "South Korea: paying a high price for an 'Economic Miracle'", in *Not Man Apart* (Friends of the Earth) San Francisco, July 1982.
10. Sadullo, Jaime R., "The threat of acid rain", in *Kapaligiran* (Newsletter of the Philippine Federation for Environmental Concern) III:2, 1984.
11. Sahabat Alam Malaysia, *The State of the Malaysian Environment 1983–84* (Penang: SAM, 1983).
12. Figures from Sahabat Alam Malaysia.
13. Sani, Sham, "Urbanisation and the atmospheric environment in SE Asia". Paper presented to Seminar on Problems of Development, Environment and the Natural Resource Crisis in Asia and the Pacific, Penang, Malaysia, October 1983.
14. See Note 13.
15. Sahabat Alam Malaysia, see note 11.
16. Sahabat Alam Malaysia, see note 11.
17. "China's economy: a survey", in *The Economist*, 1–7 August 1987.
18. Ross, Lester, *Environmental Policy in China* (Bloomington: Indiana University Press, 1988); Lynton K. Caldwell, *International Environmental Policy: Emergence and Dimensions* (Durham: Duke University Press, 1984).
19. McCormick. John, *The Global Environmental Movement:* (London: Belhaven Press, 1989).
20. Ross, see note 18.
21. Ross, see note 18.

22. Jernelöv, Arne, "Acid rain and sulfur dioxide emissions in China", in *Ambio* 12:6, 1983, p. 326.
23. Ross, see note 18
24. Jernelöv, see note 22
25. Jernelöv, see note 22
26. Zhao, Dianwu and Bozen Sun, "Air Pollution and acid rain in China" in *Ambio* 15:1, 1986, pp. 2–5.
27. Smil, see note 8.
28. Zhao and Sun, see note 26.
29. Jernelöv, see note 22.
30. Jernelöv, see note 22.
31. Kinzelbach, Wolfgang K. H., "Environmental problems in the People's Republic of China". Paper presented to the Third International Conference on Energy Use Management, West Berlin, 26–30 October 1981.
32. Long Dehuai, 1984, quoted in Ross, see note 18.
33. Qin Ling, "A discussion of China's environmental protection technology", in *Renmin Ribao* (People's Daily), 4 August 1981.
34. Smil, see note 8.
35. Smil, see note 8.
36. Centre for Science and Environment, *The State of India's Environment: A Citizen's Report* (New Delhi: CSE, 1983).
37. See note 36.
38. See note 36.
39. See note 36.
40. Sharma, A.K., "Environmental pollution in India", in *Mazingira* 7:1. 1983.
41. WHO and UNEP figures, WRI/IIED, see note 2.
42. Hardoy and Satterthwaite, see note 4.
43. Centre for Science and Environment, 1983, see note 36.
44. Centre for Science and Environment, *The State of India's Environment 1984–85: The Second Citizen's Report* (New Delhi: CSE, 1985).
45. Centre for Science and Environment, 1983, see note 36.
46. Centre for Science and Environment, 1985, see note 44.
47. See note 46.
48. See note 46.
49. Muello, Peter, "Acid rain in Latin America", in *Acid News* No. 1, March 1985.
50. See note 49.
51. Yague, Eloy, "Venezuela: acid rain 'a potential problem'" (Rome: IPS, 1983).

52. *The Citizen* (Ottawa), 3 October 1984.
53. *The Economist*, 18 February 1989.
54. WRI/IIED, see note 2.
55. *The Star* (Johannesburg), 15 February 1985.
56. See note 55.
57. See note 55.
58. ZCCML. "Environmental issues in the copper mining industry of Zambia". Unpublished paper, May 1984.
59. Perera, N. P. "Environmental problems of copper mining and refining in Zambia", in *Industry and Environment* 5:1, March 1982.

Conclusion

In about 1970 or 1971, when I was still at school in Devon, I remember reading a Sunday colour supplement story about the theoretical dangers of a rise in global temperatures brought on by the increasing use of oil and coal. The article warned that a warming of just two to three degrees could melt the polar icecaps, raising the level of the oceans to flood coastal areas, and putting much of the United Kingdom under water. There was even a map, showing the British Isles reduced to a cluster of hundreds of small islands. The whole notion seemed fantastic. Besides, the article was describing something that would only happen (if ever) some time in the next century. No need to worry about that.

I spent the summer of 1988 in the American mid-west. For weeks on end, there was no rain. Water levels in the Mississippi and the Ohio fell to record lows, stranding barges and making it possible to walk across the Ohio in some places without getting your feet wet. Mid-western farmers stood by helplessly as their crops shrivelled and died. Raging fires in the forests of the Rockies sent their smoke as far east as Chicago and Detroit. It was difficult to sleep at night without air-conditioning; stepping outside during the day was like walking into an open oven. Everywhere, grass turned yellow and brown, trees sagged in the heat, and an oppressive weight seemed to settle over the entire region. The mid-west slowed down to an exhausted crawl.

Suddenly, those distant warnings of the early 1970s seemed much more real. Some scientists held that the drought of 1988 was only part of a natural climatic cycle; others said it was the start of a global warming. As if to challenge the remaining doubters, the winter of 1988–89 turned into a series of often bizarre events: unseasonable mildness through much of Europe, record low temperatures in

Alaska and northern Canada, and floods, Arctic chills, and shirt-sleeve weather alternately in the American mid-west. Whatever the truth about all this strange weather, it had the effect of making the theoretical possibilities of a greenhouse effect much more real. Even more worrying, it was now clear that no-one was immune from the effects of environmental deterioration. It was finally impossible to escape or ignore the consequences of human interference with, and alteration of, the functioning of nature. The state of the environment was a universal issue.

Of course, this was hardly news to environmentalists. Dating from about the time of the landmark 1972 Stockholm conference on the human environment, when governments finally acknowledged the presence and persistence of environmental problems, campaigners and pressure groups had been working hard to draw the attention of policy-makers and the public to the warning signs: soil erosion, deforestation, toxic waste dumps, declining wildlife, air pollution, water pollution, and more. In the late 1960s and early 1970s, even these problems might (just) have been dismissed by many as local, minority concerns. Why should the average Londoner care about dead forests in West Germany or acid lakes in Sweden? Why should the average New Yorker care about the clearance of tropical forests in the Amazon basin or soil erosion in Ethiopia? Why should the average Kenyan or Sri Lankan care about sulphurous smogs in Los Angeles or Athens?

We can no longer dismiss such problems so easily. The decline of the environment affects everyone, irrespective of region, nation, class, age, religion, or political philosophy. It affects Marxists and libertarians, blacks and whites, Buddhists and Presbyterians, Swedes and Rwandans, young and old, rich and poor. It strikes at the very core of our entire value system, and undermines many of our assumptions about our relationship to the earth, our economic systems, our political and social priorities, our religious beliefs; in short, the way we live our lives. It demands a complete re-ordering of human values. If we cannot take the health of our physical surroundings for granted, then what can we take for granted?

Twenty years on, our perceptions are changing. Not only are many more people aware of the problems faced by the environment, but many more are aware of the consequences. In the last five years, two global issues have particularly captured more and more public attention: the destruction of the ozone layer, and the dangers of the changes that we have caused in the global climate. But perceptions began to change earlier, with a problem which still has not gone away: acid pollution. You cannot see the ozone layer, and there is still no agreement on the greenhouse effect. But you can see forests killed by acid pollution, lakes so lifeless that they have become crystal clear, buildings being eroded by acid rain and mist, and thick, yellow smogs that make it difficult to breathe. The effects of acid pollution are immediately and terribly visible.

The problem of acid pollution has helped underline the implications of environmental change. It has also revealed much about the nature of human attitudes and the quality of our political institutions.

- It has shown just how little we really know about the physics, chemistry and biology of our natural surroundings. Despite decades of research, there are still many doubts today about how acid pollution actually works. We still have no clear picture of its effects.
- The slow response to the problem has once again shown how difficult it can be – even in liberal democracies, and even when the costs of inaction are evident – for short-term political and economic thinking to respond to long-term, universal needs.
- It has raised fundamental questions about the values of orthodox economic systems, whether free enterprise or centrally planned. How can the broader, sometimes still unknown effects of environmental destruction be addressed by conventional, rational, benefit-cost analysis? How can Marxists accuse capitalists of caring little for the consequences of free enterprise when countries like Poland and Czechoslovakia choke in their own pollution?
- It has blown open the gaps and the holes in the ability of existing political institutions to respond to big problems. In almost every country that has had to face the problem of acid pollution, the inadequacies of environmental planning and administration have been revealed in the stark light of day. We just do not have the laws, the institutions or the policies that we need to effectively manage the way we use the environment.

○ It has sorely tried international relations, with normally close allies (such as the United States and Canada, and the United Kingdom and Norway) coming to diplomatic blows over the resolution of shared problems.

○ It has shown how conventional political ideology has been found seriously wanting in its ability to respond to new, more holistic policy problems, and has given added credence to the calls now being made for a realignment of the old left-right axis, and for the emergence of new green philosophies.

In short, acid pollution stands as a classic example of the consequences of economic and industrial development proceeding without due regard to external costs. Acid pollution has become a test case for the lip-service paid to environmental management by more and more governments over the past decade.

The results of this test make sobering reading. They show just how long it takes us to respond to emergencies, but also show just how much we stand to gain when we finally make the commitment. Take the example of London. Informed Britons knew nearly 140 years ago about the potential dangers of burning oil and coal. Londoners could see – and breathe – the results for themselves. Yet it took nearly another century, and the needless deaths of more than 4,000 people, before any action was taken.

The results have been truly remarkable. London smogs are now a rarity. The winter sun shines on the city once again, and those of us who long thought that the Houses of Parliament were built out of a dirty, streaked black-brown stone have been pleasantly surprised as decades of filth have been cleaned away to reveal a beautiful, seemingly rejuvenated building. But that is just one city. In other cities – Dublin, Milan, Warsaw, Prague, Los Angeles, Mexico City, Kuala Lumpur and Beijing, for example – air pollution remains a problem, and human health continues to be threatened.

Throughout Western Europe, SO_2 and NO_x emissions have been falling; in some cases they have been more than halved in just four to five years. The Swedes, the Swiss, the West Germans and the Austrians have rapidly become conscious of their environment and the dangers it faces. We can sleep easier with the knowledge that our children no longer face the same threats from lead in the air as they did before the ingredients of petrol were changed. We can begin to feel a little more certain that we are not helping to destroy a distant tree or river every time we switch on a light or go out for a drive. And we can feel a little more confident about the ability of some political systems to respond to environmental problems.

But there is still much to be done. Much of the reduction in SO_2 and NO_x emissions has been achieved at the cost of an expansion in nuclear power. The reductions made so far may not be enough to reverse the already advanced destruction of forests, rivers and lakes. There is not much sign yet of progress in the Soviet Union and Eastern Europe, although policies may be changing. Most worrying of all, south-east Asia and Latin America are developing rapidly, and their energy demand is growing by leaps and bounds. But there is no sign yet of any hard plans to avoid the mistakes of the West and build in pollution controls as industry grows. China, India, Malaysia, Brazil, Venezuela and Mexico could all be rushing head-long into the kinds of problems that have become only too familiar to West Europeans and North Americans.

We have already spent billions cutting down the sulphur and nitrogen oxides created when we burn fossil fuels. Now we are going to have to spend billions more to reduce the emissions of carbon dioxide that are pushing us towards a global greenhouse. And we are going to have to spend billions more cleaning up the mess left behind by acid pollution and global warming. And we may yet have to spend billions more cleaning up after the nuclear power industry. This all suggests that the solution to environmental management is not necessarily going to be found in short-term remedies, but rather in long-term changes in attitudes and values, in closing the gap between principle and practice, and in understanding the economic benefits of sound environmental management. It is also going to demand a long, hard look at global energy policies.

People in the middle of the next century – assuming they are more rational than we – are probably going to be looking back on the late twentieth century with a sense of awe. Why did we spend so much time and so much money, and put so much at risk, treating the symptoms of our reliance on fossil fuels rather than the disease? Why did it take us so long to realize that what we were doing was destroying the environment? Why did our institutions – government, business, universities – take so long to respond? Why did it take so long for us to reform those institutions – especially government – in order to make them more responsive to the needs of environmental planning?

> Man has too long forgotten that the earth was given to him for usufruct alone, not for consumption, still less for profligate waste. . .The ravages committed by man subvert the relations and destroy the balance which nature had established between her organized and her inorganic creations; and she avenges herself upon the intruder, by letting loose upon her defaced provinces destructive energies hitherto kept in check by organic forces destined to be his best auxiliaries, but which he has unwisely dispersed and driven from the field of action.

Those might be wise (if archaic) words for the 1990s, but they were written in 1864 by George Perkins Marsh, American diplomat and co-founder of the Smithsonian Institution. Marsh was only too aware of the dangers inherent in human attitudes to the environment. More than a century later, we are only just beginning to appreciate the true possibilities of the effects of environmental mismanagement. Hopefully we can learn by our mistakes, and learn quickly.

Index